RN Community Health Nursing
REVIEW MODULE EDITION 9.0

Contributors

Alissa Althoff, Ed.D, MSN, RN

Michelle E. Cawley, MSN, RN

Shannon Davis, MSN, BSN, RN

Sharon M. Falk, MSN, RN, CCCTM, CHSE

Mendy Gearhart, DNP, MSN, CCCE

Lori Grace, MSN, RN

Norma Jean Henry, MSN/Ed., RN

Honey C. Holman, MSN, RN

Janean Johnson, DNP, RN, CNE

Terri Lemon, DNP, MSN, RN

Beth Cusatis Phillips, PhD, RN, CNE, CHSE

Pamela Roland, MSN, MBA, RN

Consultants

Stephanie L. Belim, PhD, RN, CNE

Tracey Bousquet, BSN, RN

Lois Churchill, MN, RN

Kristi Frisbee, DNP, RN

Jenni L. Hoffman, DNP, RN, FNP-C, CLNC, FAANP

Julie Traynor, MS, RN, CNE

Director of content review: Kristen Lawler

Director of development: Derek Prater

Project management: Meri Ann Mason

Coordination of content review: Alissa Althoff, Honey C. Holman

Copy editing: Kelly Von Lunen, Tricia Lunt, Bethany Robertson, Kya Rodgers, Rebecca Her, Sam Shiel, Alethea Surland, Graphic World

Layout: Bethany Robertson, Maureen Bradshaw, Haylee Hedge, scottie. o

Illustrations: Randi Hardy, Graphic World

Online media: Brant Stacy, Ron Hanson, Britney Frerking, Trevor Lund

Interior book design: Spring Lenox

IMPORTANT NOTICE TO THE READER

User's Guide

Welcome to the Assessment Technologies Institute® RN Community Health Nursing Review Module Edition 9.0. The mission of ATI's Content Mastery Series® Review Modules is to provide user-friendly compendiums of nursing knowledge that will:

- Help you locate important information quickly.
- Assist in your learning efforts.
- Provide exercises for applying your nursing knowledge.
- Facilitate your entry into the nursing profession as a newly licensed nurse.

This newest edition of the Review Modules has been redesigned to optimize your learning experience. We've fit more content into less space and have done so in a way that will make it even easier for you to find and understand the information you need.

ORGANIZATION

Chapters in this Review Module use a nursing concepts organizing framework, beginning with an overview describing the central concept and its relevance to nursing. Subordinate themes are covered in outline form to demonstrate relationships and present the information in a clear, succinct manner. Some chapters have sections that group related concepts and contain their own overviews. These sections are included in the table of contents.

ACTIVE LEARNING SCENARIOS AND APPLICATION EXERCISES

Each chapter includes opportunities for you to test your knowledge and to practice applying that knowledge. Active Learning Scenario exercises pose a nursing scenario and then direct you to use an ATI Active Learning Template (included at the back of this book) to record the important knowledge a nurse should apply to the scenario. An example is then provided to which you can compare your completed Active Learning Template. The Application Exercises include NCLEX-style questions, such as multiple-choice and multiple-select items, providing you with opportunities to practice answering the kinds of questions you might expect to see on ATI assessments or the NCLEX. After the Application Exercises, an answer key is provided, along with rationales.

NCLEX® CONNECTIONS

To prepare for the NCLEX-RN, it is important to understand how the content in this Review Module is connected to the NCLEX-RN test plan. You can find information on the detailed test plan at the National Council of State Boards of Nursing's website, www.ncsbn.org. When reviewing content in this Review Module, regularly ask yourself, "How does this content fit into the test plan, and what types of questions related to this content should I expect?"

To help you in this process, we've included NCLEX Connections at the beginning of each unit and with each question in the Application Exercises Answer Keys. The NCLEX Connections at the beginning of each unit point out areas of the detailed test plan that relate to the content within that unit. The NCLEX Connections attached to the Application Exercises Answer Keys demonstrate how each exercise fits within the detailed content outline.

These NCLEX Connections will help you understand how the detailed content outline is organized, starting with major client needs categories and subcategories and followed by related content areas and tasks. The major client needs categories are:

- Safe and Effective Care Environment
  - Management of Care
  - Safety and Infection Control
- Health Promotion and Maintenance
- Psychosocial Integrity
- Physiological Integrity
  - Basic Care and Comfort
  - Pharmacological and Parenteral Therapies
  - Reduction of Risk Potential
  - Physiological Adaptation

An NCLEX Connection might, for example, alert you that content within a unit is related to:

- Safety and Infection Control
  - Home Safety
    - Assess need for client home modifications.

QSEN COMPETENCIES

As you use the Review Modules, you will note the integration of the Quality and Safety Education for Nurses (QSEN) competencies throughout the chapters. These competencies are integral components of the curriculum of many nursing programs in the United States and prepare you to provide safe, high-quality care as a newly licensed nurse. Icons appear to draw your attention to the six QSEN competencies.

Safety: The minimization of risk factors that could cause injury or harm while promoting quality care and maintaining a secure environment for clients, self, and others.

Patient-Centered Care: The provision of caring and compassionate, culturally sensitive care that addresses clients' physiological, psychological, sociological, spiritual, and cultural needs, preferences, and values.

Evidence-Based Practice: The use of current knowledge from research and other credible sources, on which to base clinical judgment and client care.

Informatics: The use of information technology as a communication and information-gathering tool that supports clinical decision-making and scientifically based nursing practice.

Quality Improvement: Care related and organizational processes that involve the development and implementation of a plan to improve health care services and better meet clients' needs.

Teamwork and Collaboration: The delivery of client care in partnership with multidisciplinary members of the health care team to achieve continuity of care and positive client outcomes.

ICONS

Icons are used throughout the Review Module to draw your attention to particular areas. Keep an eye out for these icons.

N This icon is used for NCLEX Connections.

G This icon indicates gerontological considerations, or knowledge specific to the care of older adult clients.

Qs This icon is used for content related to safety and is a QSEN competency. When you see this icon, take note of safety concerns or steps that nurses can take to ensure client safety and a safe environment.

QPCC This icon is a QSEN competency that indicates the importance of a holistic approach to providing care.

QEBP This icon, a QSEN competency, points out the integration of research into clinical practice.

QI This icon is a QSEN competency and highlights the use of information technology to support nursing practice.

QQI This icon is used to focus on the QSEN competency of integrating planning processes to meet clients' needs.

QTC This icon highlights the QSEN competency of care delivery using an interprofessional approach.

SDoH This icon highlights content related to social determinants of health.

M◇ This icon appears at the top-right of pages and indicates availability of an online media supplement, such as a graphic, animation, or video. If you have an electronic copy of the Review Module, this icon will appear alongside clickable links to media supplements. If you have a hard copy version of the Review Module, visit www.atitesting.com for details on how to access these features.

FEEDBACK

ATI welcomes feedback regarding this Review Module. Please provide comments to comments@atitesting.com.

As needed updates to the Review Modules are identified, changes to the text are made for subsequent printings of the book and for subsequent releases of the electronic version. For the printed books, print runs are based on when existing stock is depleted. For the electronic versions, a number of factors influence the update schedule. As such, ATI encourages faculty and students to refer to the Review Module addendums for information on what updates have been made. These addendums—which are available in the Help/FAQs on the student site and the Resources/eBooks & Active Learning on the faculty site—are updated regularly and always include the most current information on updates to the Review Modules.

Table of Contents

When reviewing the following chapter, keep in mind the relevant topics and tasks of the NCLEX outline, in particular:

Management of Care

ADVOCACY: Utilize advocacy resources appropriately.

ETHICAL PRACTICE: Practice in a manner consistent with the code of ethics for nurses.

PERFORMANCE IMPROVEMENT (QUALITY IMPROVEMENT): Define performance improvement/quality assurance activities.

Health Promotion and Maintenance

HEALTH PROMOTION/DISEASE PREVENTION: Educate the client on actions to promote/maintain health and prevent disease.

HEALTH SCREENING: Perform targeted screening assessments (e.g., vision, nutrition).

Overview of Community Health Nursing

Community health nursing is a population-focused approach to planning, delivering, and evaluating nursing care. Community health nursing is a broad field that allows nurses to practice in a wide variety of settings. Community health nurses promote the health and welfare of clients across the lifespan and from diverse populations.

Foundations of community health nursing

- Concepts related to public health are evident throughout history as provisions were made to care for the poor or displaced. Advances in knowledge about health led to appropriate education of providers and regulation of water and other environmental factors.
- The Public Health Service was developed in 1798, and nursing care in homes was implemented in the early 1800s. Later in the century, efforts began to establish local health boards to monitor disease, promote health, and collect statistics about the community.
- Multiple theories and specific definitions of care guide nursing practice in the community.

COMMUNITY HEALTH NURSING THEORIES

- **Systems thinking** studies how an individual or unit interacts with other organizations or systems. Systems thinking is useful in examining cause and effect relationships.
- **Upstream thinking** is used to focus on interventions that promote health or prevent illness, as opposed to medical treatment models that focus on care after an individual becomes ill.
- Nursing theory provides the basis for care of the community and family. Theorists have developed sound principles to guide nurses in providing high-quality care. Examples of nursing theories appropriate for community health include the following.

Nightingale's environmental theory

- Highlights the relationship between an individual's environment and health
- Depicts health as a continuum
- Emphasizes preventive care

Health belief model

- Purpose is to predict or explain health behaviors
- Assumes that preventive health actions are taken primarily for the purpose of avoiding disease
- Emphasizes change at the individual level
  - Describes the likelihood of taking an action to avoid disease based on the following
  - Perceived susceptibility, seriousness, and threat of a disease
  - Modifying factors (demographics, knowledge level)
  - Cues to action (media campaigns, disease effect on family/friends, recommendations from health care professionals)
  - Perceived benefits minus perceived barriers to taking action

Milio's framework for prevention

- Complements the health belief model
- Emphasizes change at the community level
- Identifies relationship between health deficits and availability of health-promoting resources
- Theorizes that behavior changes within a large number of people can ultimately lead to social change

Pender's health promotion model

- Similar to Health Belief Model
- Does not consider health risk as a factor that provokes change
- Examines factors that affect individual actions to promote and protect health
  - Personal factors (biological, psychological, sociocultural), behaviors, abilities, self-efficacy
  - Feelings, benefits, barriers, and characteristics associated with the action
  - Attitudes of others, and competing demands and preferences

Transtheoretical model (TTM) or stages of change (SOC)

Theorizes that change occurs over time, and in six distinct stages:
- Precontemplation, where the individual is unaware of the need to change
- Contemplation, where the individual considers change, and weighs the benefits with costs
- Preparation, where the individual plans to take action
- Action
- Maintenance, where the individual implements actions to continue the behavior
- Termination, when conscious efforts to continue the health behavior are no longer needed because the individual is consistent. Most clients never reach this point.

Precaution adoption process model

- Similar to the TTM and SOC models
- Includes a stage of being unengaged regarding an issue between the stages of being unaware and contemplating action
- Does not include a termination stage

ESSENTIALS OF COMMUNITY NURSING

- **Determinants of health** are client or environmental factors that influence the client's health. These can include nutrition, social support and stress, education, finances, transportation and housing, biology and genetics, and personal health practices. For additional information, refer to **CHAPTER 2: SOCIAL DETERMINANTS OF HEALTH (SDOH)**.
- **Health indicators** (mortality rates, disease prevalence, levels of physical activity, BMI, tobacco or other substance use) describe the health status of a community and serve as targets for the improvement of a community's health. Qᴸ
- **Nurses** determine a community's health by examining the degree to which the community's collective health needs are identified and met.
- **Community** is a group of people and institutions that share geographic, civic, and/or social parameters. Communities vary in their characteristics and health needs.
- Community health nursing involves a synthesis of nursing and public health theory.
- The goals of community health nursing (also called community-oriented nursing) are to promote, preserve, and maintain the health of populations by the delivery of health services to individuals, families, and groups, in order to influence "community health."
- Community health nurses are nurses who practice in the community. They usually have a facility from which they work (community health clinic, county health department), but their practice is not limited to institutional settings. Care is often delivered in a setting that is part of the client's environment (home, school, workplace) but is focused on the community population and subpopulations.
- The community or a population (an aggregate who shares one or more personal characteristics) within the community is the "client" in community health nursing. Qᴾᶜᶜ
- Community-based nurses can develop relationships with clients while working directly with individuals who have acute and chronic conditions and their families.

Public health nursing

- Public health nursing is population-focused and involves a combination of nursing knowledge with social and public health sciences. The goal of public health nursing is promoting health and preventing disease.
- Public health provides 10 essential services, one of which is to conduct research to gain new knowledge and solutions to public health problems. The remainder fall under the three core functions of public health, according to the CDC.

ASSESSMENT: Using systematic methods to monitor the health of a population
- Monitor health status to identify community health problems.
- Diagnose and investigate health problems and health hazards in the community.

POLICY DEVELOPMENT: Developing laws and practices to promote the health of a population based on scientific evidence
- Inform, educate, and empower people about health issues.
- Mobilize community partnerships to identify and solve health problems.
- Develop policies and plans that support individual and community health efforts.

ASSURANCE: Making sure adequate health care personnel and services are accessible, especially to those who might not normally have them Qᴸ
- Enforce laws and regulations that protect health and ensure safety.
- Link people to needed personal health services and ensure the provision of health care when otherwise unavailable.
- Ensure a competent public health and personal health care workforce.
- Evaluate effectiveness, accessibility, and quality of personal and population-based health services.

For additional information about public health nursing, refer to **CHAPTER 5: PRACTICE SETTINGS AND NURSING ROLES IN THE COMMUNITY**.

1.1 Community health nursing

	Community-oriented nursing	Community-based nursing
FOCUS OF CARE	Aggregates, communities, populations (public health) Can include at-risk or unserved individuals and families	Individuals and families
PRIMARY GOAL	Health promotion and disease prevention	Management of acute or chronic conditions
NURSING ACTIVITIES	Usually indirect (program management) Can include direct care of at-risk individuals and populations	Direct (one-on-one) Illness care: Management of acute and chronic conditions in settings where individuals, families, and groups live, work, and "attend" (schools, camps, prisons)

Population-focused nursing

- Population-focused nursing includes assessing to determine needs, intervening to protect and promote health, and preventing disease within a specific population (individuals at risk for hypertension, individuals who do not have health insurance, individuals who have a specific knowledge deficit). Qᴾᴄᴄ
- The Public Health Intervention Wheel is a widely used model for the 10 essential public health services and is available through the Minnesota Department of Health website and the CDC website.
- Community partnership occurs when community members, agencies, and businesses actively participate in the processes of health promotion and disease prevention. The development of community partnerships is critical to the accomplishment of health promotion and disease prevention strategies.

KEY PRINCIPLES OF PUBLIC HEALTH NURSING

- Emphasize primary prevention.
- Work to achieve the greatest good for the largest number of individuals.
- Recognize that the client is a partner in health.
- Use resources wisely to promote the best outcomes.

Principles guiding community health nursing

Factors to consider when providing community health nursing practice include the following.
- Ethics
- Advocacy
- Evidence-based practice
- Quality
- Professional collaboration and communication

ETHICS

- The Public Health Code of Ethics identifies the ethical practice of public health. Ethical considerations include preventing harm, doing no harm, promoting good, respecting both individual and community rights, respecting autonomy and diversity, and providing confidentiality, competency, trustworthiness, and advocacy.
- Community health nurses are concerned with protecting, promoting, preserving, and maintaining health, as well as preventing disease. These concerns reflect the ethical principle of promoting good and preventing harm. Balancing individual rights vs. rights of community groups is a challenge.
- Community health nurses address the challenges of autonomy and providing ethical care. Client rights include the right to information disclosure, privacy, informed consent, information confidentiality, and participation in treatment decisions.

- As nurses participate in research in the community setting, it is important to use ethical decision-making to promote client rights.
- Public health nurses can apply ethical principles through core functions as they collect and manage information (assessment), develop policies that are in the best interest of the people in an area (policy development), and create interventions that promote healthcare equality across population groups (assurance).

ADVOCACY

Client advocate is one role of the community health nurse. The nurse plays the role of informer, supporter, and mediator for the client. The following are basic to client advocacy.
- Clients are autonomous beings who have the right to make decisions affecting their own health and welfare.
- Clients have the right to expect a nurse–client relationship that is based on trust, collaboration, and shared respect; related to health; and considerate of their thoughts and feelings.
- Clients are responsible for their own health.
- It is the nurse's responsibility to advocate for resources or services that meet the client's health care needs.
- Advocating for clients requires assertiveness, placing priority on the client's values, and willingness to progress through the chain of command for resolution.
- Nurses act as advocates for communities and populations through efforts to change health care systems and improve quality of life. An example of public health advocacy includes nurses working to promote access to clinics for individuals who live in rural communities.

1.2 Application of ethical principles to community health nursing

Respect for autonomy

Individuals select those actions that fulfill their goals.

SITUATIONS: Respecting a client's right to self-determination (making a decision not to pursue chemotherapy)

Nonmaleficence

No harm is done when applying standards of care.

SITUATIONS: Developing plans of care that include a system for monitoring and evaluating outcomes

Beneficence

Maximize possible benefits and minimize possible harms.

SITUATIONS: Assessing costs, risks and benefits when planning interventions

Distributive justice

Fair distribution of the benefits and burden in society is based on the needs and contributions of its members.

SITUATIONS: Determining eligibility for health care services based on income and fiscal resources

EVIDENCE-BASED PRACTICE

Evidence-based practice involves using best practices, expert opinion, and client preferences to change the delivery of client care. The goal is to improve client outcomes.

Data

- The nurse should appraise data collected from research to measure whether bias was minimal (**quality**); the number of studies, participants, or strength of effect (**quantity**); and whether the results are repeatable (**consistency**). The nurse then analyzes the data for application to practice. Q**EBP**
- Data is also classified to determine the strength of the information. The nurse should seek the highest level of evidence available and choose information that is validated by systematic peer-review.·

In the community

- Evidence-based practice improves public health as nurses develop policies to improve the health of specific groups. The public health nurse can use evidence to provide new solutions for groups of people (assessment), provide information to communities (policy development) and evaluate the effectiveness of the health care environment for groups (assurance).
- An example of evidence-based practice in community health includes the use of high levels of evidence to support media campaigns regarding immunization guidelines.
- The Community Preventive Services Task Force (CPSTF) produces a guide that reviews health promotion and disease prevention guidelines compared to the available evidence. The task force then determines whether there is sufficient or strong evidence to implement an intervention and lists which ones have insufficient evidence to show that they are effective.
- The nurse must consider several factors when applying evidence to practice: cost, benefit to the client, client satisfaction, safety, and client specific factors, such as culture and demographics. An intervention that is appropriate on the client or family level might not work when the nurse is caring for communities or populations of people.
- Nurses in the community setting can contribute to the body of evidence by implementing research studies in the practice setting and in collaboration with educational institutions, health care facilities, and through community-based participatory research (CBPR).
  - CBPR includes partners, professionals, and community residents in identifying health issues and intervening.
  - The CBPR approach fosters support from community members, develops leadership within the community, and promotes a positive collaborative relationship with health professionals.

QUALITY

- Quality assurance, quality improvement, and quality management are part of improvement of health care. Detailed information about quality improvement is available in the Nursing Leadership and Management Review Module.
- Quality care is promoted through licensure and credentialing of health care providers, adherence to facility policies, professional development, and compliance with legal guidelines. Specialty certification is available for many community health roles. Q**ι**
- Quality report cards for managed care and public health organizations provide data about the effectiveness of care. Community health report cards can include health profiles, needs assessments, information about quality of life, and health status.
- Nurses can use information from quality report cards in developing or revising strategies for care of communities. An example of increasing quality in community health is educating clients who have diabetes mellitus on how frequently their providers should perform glycosylated hemoglobin testing.

Total quality management (TQM)

TQM is an approach that seeks to improve quality and performance which meets or exceeds expectations.

Continuous quality improvement (CQI)

- CQI is an approach to quality management that emphasizes the organization and its processes and systems and uses objective data to analyze and improve processes.
- Public health nurses follow the continuous quality improvement process in carrying out roles of assessment, assurance, and policy development on an ongoing basis. Nurses can evaluate quality by examining the following aspects of care.
  - **Effectiveness:** providing services to those who will benefit
  - **Timeliness:** reducing waits and harmful delays in providing and receiving care
  - **Client-centered:** ensuring client values guide decision-making
  - **Equity:** providing equal care without discriminating against gender, race, sexual orientation, socioeconomic status
  - **Safety:** avoiding injuries to clients from the care intended to help them
  - **Efficiency:** avoiding waste in supplies, ideas, energy

PROFESSIONAL COLLABORATION AND COMMUNICATION

- Nurses in various community settings use communication skills in caring for individuals, collaborating in teams and groups, interacting with other professionals, and informing the public and stakeholders.
- The nurse facilitates communication with the client through transfers from one level of care to another, across the continuum of care.
- Nurse leaders use professional communication in roles such as mentoring, coaching employees, managing conflict, and supervising programs.
- Community health nurses should take care to use clear language with a respectful tone when using written, electronic, or print correspondence.
- The nurse should incorporate knowledge about variations in verbal and nonverbal communication, literacy needs, and client preferences when interacting with clients and groups.
- As with all aspects of health care, the nurse in the community setting is bound by laws regulating privacy and confidentiality in all forms of communication.

BENEFITS OF PROFESSIONAL COMMUNICATION

- Increased client adherence to prescribed treatment plan
- Reduced admissions to acute care
- Reduced cost of care
- Shared decision-making with client and family
- Reduced medication errors

Health Promotion and Disease Prevention

- The terms health promotion and disease prevention are often used interchangeably. They refer to strategies which affect an individual's overall health, to promote good health to reduce the overall risk for disease, and to reduce the risk for specific conditions, such as motor vehicle injuries and influenza.
- National health goals guide nurses in developing health promotion strategies to improve individual and community health.
- Community health nurses participate in three levels of prevention: primary, secondary, and tertiary.

HEALTH PROMOTION

- Healthy People national health goals are derived from scientific data and trends collected during the prior decade. These goals are based on those issues that are considered major risks to the health and wellness of the United States' population. Q̵EBP
  - ○ Healthy People was initiated in 1979, and, every 10 years, publishes the national health objectives that serve as a guide for promoting health and preventing disease.
  - ○ Healthy People is coordinated by the U.S. Department of Health and Human Services, along with other federal agencies, and transitioned to Healthy People 2030 in August 2020.
  - ○ Healthy People serves as a measure for quality of health. The national health goals guide the nurse in developing health promotion strategies to improve individual and community health.
  - ○ Healthy People initiatives have shown that implementing health promotion and disease prevention strategies leads to decreased expense for healthcare and improves the length of the client's lifespan.
  - ○ Healthy People objectives include impacting the following focus areas.
    - Access to health services
    - Adolescent health
    - Chronic kidney disease
    - Disability
    - Genomics
    - Global health
    - Health-related quality of life and well-being
    - Hearing and other sensory or communication disorders
    - Nutrition and weight status
    - Older adults
    - Oral health
    - Preparedness
    - Family planning
    - Food safety
    - Mental health and mental disorders
    - Medical product safety
    - Lesbian, gay, bisexual, and transgender health
    - Substance abuse
    - Sleep health
- The community health nurse actively helps people to change their lifestyles in order to move toward a state of optimal health (physical and psychosocial).
- Preventive services include health education and counseling based on scientific evidence, immunizations, taking preventive medication, lifestyle changes, and other actions that aim to prevent a potential disease or disability.
- The community health nurse provides preventive services in multiple community settings.
- The community health nurse is often responsible for planning and implementing screening programs for at-risk populations.
- Successful screening programs provide accurate, reliable results, can be inexpensively and quickly administered to large groups, and produce few if any adverse effects.
- The nurse should evaluate a potential screening method to determine whether it can be used consistently (reliability), it demonstrates accuracy of measurement (validity), and how effective it is at identifying an individual with a particular condition (predictive value).

DISEASE PREVENTION

Primary prevention

Prevention of the initial occurrence of disease or injury
- Nutrition education
- Family planning and sex education
- Smoking cessation education
- Communicable disease prevention education
- Education about health and hygiene issues to specific groups (day care workers, restaurant workers)
- Safety education (seat belt use, helmet use)
- Prenatal classes
- Providing immunizations
- Advocating for access to health care, healthy environments

Secondary prevention

Early detection and treatment of disease with the goal of limiting severity and adverse effects
- Community assessments
- Disease surveillance (communicable diseases)
- Screenings
- Cancer (breast, cervical, testicular, prostate, colorectal)
- Diabetes mellitus
- Hypertension
- Hypercholesterolemia
- Sensory impairments
- Tuberculosis
- Lead exposure
- Genetic disorders/metabolic deficiencies in newborns
- Control of outbreaks of communicable diseases

Tertiary prevention

Reducing the limitations of disability and promoting rehabilitation following health alterations
- Maximization of recovery after an injury or illness (rehabilitation)
- Nutrition counseling for management of Crohn's disease
- Exercise rehabilitation
- Case management (chronic illness, mental illness)
- Physical and occupational therapy
- Support groups
- Exercise for a client who has hypertension (individual)

Active Learning Scenario

A case manager at a dialysis clinic is using the Health Belief Model (HBM) to guide discussions with clients who have not been adhering to the treatment plan. Use the *ATI Active Learning Template: Basic Concept* to complete this item.

RELATED CONTENT

Describe two components of the HBM.

UNDERLYING PRINCIPLES

Name two cues to action that could influence an individual to take a positive action related to health.

NURSING INTERVENTIONS

Name two interventions the nurse could implement with clients who have kidney disease to promote individual adherence to the treatment plan.

Active Learning Scenario Key

Using the ATI Active Learning Template: Basic Concept

RELATED CONTENT

Components of the HBM:
- Predict or explain health behaviors
- Assumed individuals take actions because they want to avoid negative health consequences
- Focuses on changes at the individual level

UNDERLYING PRINCIPLES

Cues to action:
- TV or newspaper ads about health promotion
- Seeing the effect of disease on significant others
- Advice and counseling from members of the interprofessional team

NURSING INTERVENTIONS
- Provide videos or pictures that show damage to the body from kidney failure.
- Ask clients who have kidney disease to form a support group and discuss health promotion.
- Provide simple handouts about diet and self-care related to kidney disease.
- Ask the clients if friends and family can join discussions about the treatment plan to provide input.
- Determine whether the client has concerns about kidney disease and the risk of complications.
- Review the client's demographic information about the client to determine possible barriers or health disparities.
- Assist the client in establishing positive relationships with health care team members.

Ⓝ *NCLEX® Connection: Health Promotion and Maintenance, Health Promotion/Disease Prevention*

Application Exercises

1. Determine to which of the three core functions each essential service listed below belongs: Assessment, Policy Development, Assurance.

   A. Monitor health status

   B. Evaluate effectiveness

   C. Enforce law and regulations for health and safety

   D. Diagnose and invesetiage health problems

   E. Inform, educate, and empower people

   F. Link individuals to health services

   G. Develop policies and plans

   H. Ensure competent health workforce

   I. Mobilize community partnerships

2. A nurse manager at a community agency is developing content for an orientation program for newly hired nurses to highlight the differences between community-based and community-oriented nursing activities. Sort the following activity with the type of community nursing: Community-based or Community-oriented.

   A. A home health nurse performing wound care for a client who is immobile

   B. An occupational health nurse providing classes on body mechanics at a local industrial plant

   C. A school nurse teaching a student who has asthma about medications

   D. A parish nurse teaching a class on low-sodium cooking techniques

   E. A mental health nurse discussing stress mangement techniques with a support group

3. A public health nurse is reviewing the outcomes of an exercise program at various locations. Which of the following aspects of care does this finding evaluate?

   A. Timeliness

   B. Client-centered

   C. Equity

   D. Safety

4. A nurse is advocating for local leaders to place a newly-approved community health clinic in an area of the city that has fewer resources than other areas. The nurse is advocating for the leaders to uphold which of the following ethical principles?

   A. Distributive justice

   B. Fidelity

   C. Respect for autonomy

   D. Veracity

5. A community health nurse is planning to implement health programs with several populations in the local area. Sort the following programs with the level of prevention it meets: Primary, Secondary, or Tertiary.

   A. Performing a home safety check at a client's home

   B. Teaching health nutrition to clients who have hypertension

   C. Providing influenza immunizations to employees at a local preschool

   D. Implenting a program to notify individuals exposed to a communicale disease

   E. Reviewing colonscopy screening guidelines at a community center.

Application Exercises Key

1. **ASSESSMENT**: A, D; **POLICY DEVELOPMENT**: E, G, I;
   ASSURANCE: B, C, F, H;

   Nurses recognize and analyze cues through assessment activities using systematic methods to monitor health status and diagnose and investigate health problems in the community. Nurses prioritize hypotheses and generate solutions through policy development activities; development of laws and practices based on scientific evidence to inform, educate, and empower individuals about health issues; mobilization of community partnerships; and development of policies and plans that support health efforts. Nurses take action and evaluate outcomes through assurance activities, such as ensuring adequate health care personnel and services are available; enforcing laws and regulations for health and safety; linking individuals to health services; ensuring a competent health workforce; and evaluating health services.

   Ⓝ *NCLEX® Connection: Health Promotion and Maintenance, Health Promotion/Disease Prevention*

2. **COMMUNITY-BASED**: A, C;
   COMUNITY-ORIENTED: B, D, E;

   When generating solutions to develop content about community-based and community-oriented nursing activities, the nurse identifies management of acute and chronic conditions with individuals in a community setting as a community-based nursing activity. The nurse identifies providing care to a population to prevent disease and promote health as a community-oriented nursing activity.

   Ⓝ *NCLEX® Connection: Health Promotion and Maintenance, Health Promotion/Disease Prevention*

3. C. **CORRECT:** When evaluating outcomes of an exercise program, the nurse recognizes that evaluating client outcomes across geographic locations helps to validate that the program was equitable. The nurse recognizes that examining data based on gender, ethnicity, and socioeconomic status also ensure equity across those variables.

   Ⓝ *NCLEX® Connection: Health Promotion and Maintenance, Health Promotion/Disease Prevention*

4. A. **CORRECT:** When taking actions to advocate for resources, the nurse is upholding the ethical principle of distributive justice, which is the fair distribution of benefits and burden in society.

   Ⓝ *NCLEX® Connection: Management of Care, Ethical Practice*

5. **PRIMARY**: C; **SECONDARY**: A, D, E; **TERTIARY**: B;

   When generating solutions to implement health programs, the nurse should plan to provide influenza immunizations as a primary prevention program, because the goal is to prevent the occurrence of disease or injury. The nurse should plan to perform home safety checks, notify individuals exposed to a communicable disease, and review colonoscopy screening guidelines as secondary prevention programs, because the goal is early detection and treatment of disease. The nurse should plan to teach healthy nutrition to clients with hypertension as a tertiary prevention program, because the goal is reducing disability and promoting rehabilitation to individuals who have a health condition.

   Ⓝ *NCLEX® Connection: Health Promotion and Maintenance, Health Promotion/Disease Prevention*

NCLEX® Connections

When reviewing the following chapter, keep in mind the relevant topics and tasks of the NCLEX outline, in particular:

Management of Care

CASE MANAGEMENT: Explore resources available to assist the client with achieving or maintaining independence.

Safety and Infection Control

ACCIDENT/ERROR/INJURY PREVENTION: Protect client from injury.

HOME SAFETY: Evaluate client care environment for fire/environmental hazard.

Health Promotion and Maintenance

DEVELOPMENTAL STAGES AND TRANSITIONS: Recognize cultural and religious influences that may impact family functioning.

HEALTH SCREENING: Perform health history/health and risk assessments.

LIFESTYLE CHOICES: Evaluate client alternative or homeopathic health care practices.

HEALTH PROMOTION/DISEASE PREVENTION: Plan and/or participate in community health education.

Psychosocial Integrity

CULTURAL AWARENESS/CULTURAL INFLUENCES ON HEALTH: Evaluate and document how client language needs were met.

STRESS MANAGEMENT: Implement measures to reduce environmental stressors.

Social Determinants of Health

Social determinants of health (SDOH) are factors within a community or defined location that affect individual health. These are divided into six categories: social and community context, neighborhood and built environment, health and health care, economic stability, food and nutrition, and education. These factors impact risks and outcomes associated with health, daily functioning, and quality of life.

Health disparities are preventable differences in the burden of disease, injury, violence, or opportunities to achieve optimal health that are experienced by socially disadvantaged populations. Vulnerable populations are at greater risk for poor health status, limited access to health care services and nutritious foods, and significant disparities in life expectancy, morbidity, and mortality.

Racial inequalities are associated with vulnerabilities. Inequities impact access to a range of social and economic benefits such as housing, education, wealth and employment. Racial and ethnic minority groups experience higher rates of illness and death across a wide range of health conditions when compared to their White counterparts.

Nurses can use the concept of social justice to ensure that vulnerable populations are included in equitable allocation of resources within a community to reduce health disparities.

Social and Community Context

- The Office of Minority Health has requirements for culturally and linguistically appropriate services (CLAS). CLAS standards promote development of a health care workforce that can respond effectively to the needs of a diverse client population.
- CLAS standards include providing language assistance and information to a client in their preferred language throughout the delivery of health care.
- CLAS standards promote ongoing improvement and accountability for culturally appropriate care.
- Congruency between culture and health care is essential to the well-being of the client. The link between health beliefs and practices is greatly influenced by an individual's culture.
- It is important to assess cultural beliefs and practices when developing a plan of care. Qᴘᴄᴄ
  - Understand that there are variations within each culture.
  - Consider the uniqueness of each client.
  - Become familiar with cultures represented in the local community.

Cultural competence: Cultural competence is a skill the nurse develops in learning to respect individual dignity and preferences, as well as acknowledging cultural differences.
- The provision of culturally competent care requires nurses to be responsive to the needs of clients from various cultures. Culturally competent care is guided by these dimensions.
  - **Cultural humility:** Appreciating, understanding, and partnering with clients from cultures different than the nurse's culture
  - **Cultural preservation:** Assisting the client to maintain traditional values and practices
  - **Cultural accommodation:** Supporting and facilitating the client's use of cultural practices that are beneficial to the client's health
  - **Cultural repatterning:** Assisting the client to modify cultural practices that are not beneficial to the client's health
  - **Cultural brokering:** Advocating, mediating, negotiating, and intervening between the client's culture and health care culture on behalf of the client
- Nurse leaders can use cultural competency in creating and working with a diverse workforce that can meet the needs of a diverse client population.

CULTURAL ASSESSMENT

A cultural assessment provides information to the health care provider about the effect of culture on communication, space and physical contact, time, social organization, and environmental control factors. It is important for the nurse to become familiar with cultures represented in the local community and how cultural factors can affect the effectiveness of nursing interventions.

- Prior to collecting information about a client's culture, the nurse should perform a self-assessment and ask the following questions to prevent personal bias.
  - Am I aware of my culture and views about other cultures?
  - Am I able to perform a culturally sensitive assessment?
  - Do I have the knowledge necessary to develop culturally appropriate nursing interventions?
  - What is my goal in learning about diverse populations?

Environmental control

- Indicates the belief in how the environment affects the individual.
- Individuals who believe that the environment can be mastered to affect health status will actively engage in health promotion, disease prevention, and treatment.
- Individuals who feel that their outcome is predetermined and they cannot affect it are not as likely to engage in health-related behaviors.
- Individuals who believe in harmony with the environment are more likely to look for naturalistic solutions to correct what is perceived as an imbalance between the mind, body, and spirit.

Time orientation

- Describes whether an individual focuses more on the past, the present, or the future.
- Individuals who focus on the past or present can have little interest in health promotion behaviors, which are described as having benefit in the future.

Social organization

- Describes the significance of individual members of a family or the family as a whole. Social organization often affects how decisions are made within a family or group.
- The nurse should understand that decisions about a client's health might be made by an individual other than the client, or by the group. The nurse should plan to include in teaching and decision-making any individuals the client dictates as important to the process.
- The nurse should understand that the client might make decisions based on the greater good of the family or group rather than self, and should respect the client's choice.

Health beliefs and practices

Varies among cultures. Whatever an individual believes is the cause of impaired health will affect actions the individual will take to treat or prevent disease.

- **Biomedical beliefs** about illness focus on identifying a cause for every effect on the body, that the body functions like a machine. This is the basis for the way the majority of medical facilities in the U.S. function and is based on identifying a biophysical cause and treatment for health problems.
- **Naturalistic beliefs** about illness relate the individual as a part of nature or creation. An imbalance in nature is believed to cause disease. This is the basis of Eastern or Chinese medicine. Several other cultures, such as the Mexican culture, follow the hot-cold theory of balance in relation to health and illness that accompanies this belief framework.
- **Magico-religious beliefs** about illness link health to supernatural forces, or good and evil. This includes belief in faith healing used by some Christian religions, or voodoo and witchcraft practices used in Caribbean nations.

Biological variations in health

- Can be linked to genetic ties from biological relatives
- Include growth and development, laboratory test findings, skin color, and susceptibility to disease

CULTURAL ASSESSMENT PARAMETERS

- Ethnic background
- Religious preferences
- Family structure
- Language and literacy needs
- Communication needs
- Education
- Cultural values
- Food patterns
- Health promotion and maintenance practices
- Types of health practitioners used
- Medicines, remedies, treatments, and therapies used

STEPS OF DATA COLLECTION

- The first step of the cultural assessment is collection of self-identifying data about the client's ethnic background, religious preference, family structure, food patterns, and health practices.
- Next, the nurse should pose questions that address the client's perceptions of their health needs.
- The final step of the data collection process is identification of how cultural factors can affect the effectiveness of nursing interventions.

NURSING INTERVENTIONS

- Establish partnerships with community organizations and engagement
  - Neighborhood associations
  - Social media pages for information exchange
  - After school and extracurricular activities
- Identify programs that aid in times of stress/crisis
  - Emergency housing
  - Financial assistance
  - Vulnerable populations

CONVEYING CULTURAL SENSITIVITY

- Address clients by their last names, unless the client gives the nurse permission to use other names.
- Introduce yourself by name and explain your position.
- Be authentic and honest about what is known or not known about a client's culture.
- Use culturally sensitive language.
- Find out what clients know about their health problems and treatments and determine the client's intent to adhere to the prescribed treatment plan.
- Incorporate clients' preferences and practices into care when possible.
- Do not make assumptions about clients.
- Encourage clients to ask about anything that they might not understand.
- Respect clients' values, beliefs, and practices.
- Show respect for clients' support systems.
- Provide health teaching materials in the client's primary language and at the recommended readability level.

USING AN INTERPRETER

- The nurse should use an interpreter when it is difficult for a nurse or client to understand the other's language.
- Interpreters should have knowledge of health-related terminology.
- The use of family members as interpreters is not advisable because clients might need privacy in discussing sensitive matters. Family members can lack objectivity when relaying information to or from the client, and the family member can have difficulty understanding medical terminology.
- The nurse should consider client preferences when selecting the age and gender of an interpreter.
- Interpreters should not be from the same community as the client.
- Differences in socioeconomic status, religious affiliation, educational level, and spoken dialect can result in translation barriers.
- Federal government mandates require agencies to have a plan that will improve access to federal health care programs for individuals who have limited English proficiency.
- Subcultures might have conflict.

Neighborhood and Built Environment

Neighborhood and built environment relates to the quality of the air, land, water, and other surroundings with which people come into contact. It addresses positive factors such as the presence of sidewalks, bike lanes, and green space and well as detrimental factors such as crime and violence as well as area industrial complexes which can decrease the quality of air, ground, and water. Additionally, this refers to the accessibility of transportation and grocery stores that sell healthy foods.

- Nurses identify environmental health risk, participate in research, and use advocacy to improve environmental quality.
- Nurses can contribute to environmental health by using environmentally friendly practices and materials, as well as providing information to the public about environmental health.
- Toxicology considers how exposure to chemicals can have negative effects on health. Nurses use toxicological information to understand the specific effects that environmental hazards have on populations at risk or following exposure. Data is available through the National Library of Medicine at www.nlm.nih.gov.

DATA COLLECTION

- Accessible, safe, and clean parks and public spaces
- Homes and workplaces built to code
- Low crime rates
- Access to potable water and sewage facilities
- Safe traffic patterns

ENVIRONMENTAL RISKS

Toxins: lead, pesticides, mercury, solvents, asbestos, and radon

Air pollution: carbon monoxide, particulate matter, ozone, lead, aerosols, nitrogen dioxide, sulfur dioxide, and tobacco smoke

Water pollution: wastes, erosion after mining or timbering, and run-off from chemicals added to the soil

Contamination: food and food products with bacteria, pesticides, radiation, and medication (growth hormones or antibiotics)

ROLES FOR NURSES

- Facilitate public participation in measures to improve the environment.
- Perform individual and population risk assessments.
- Implement risk communication.
- Conduct epidemiological investigations.
- Participate in policy development.

ASSESSMENT

The "I PREPARE" mnemonic is one method of determining current and past environmental exposures. Qs

I: Investigate: potential exposures

P: Present work: exposures, use of personal protective equipment, location of safety data sheets (SDSs), hazardous materials brought home from work on clothing, trends

R: Residence: age of home, heating, recent remodeling, chemical storage, water

E: Environmental concerns: air, water, soil, industries in the neighborhood, waste site or landfill nearby

P: Past work: exposures, farm work, military, volunteer, seasonal, length of work

A: Activities: hobbies, activities, gardening, fishing, hunting, soldering, melting, burning, eating, pesticides, alternative healing/medicines

R: Referrals and resources: Environmental Protection Agency, Agency for Toxic Substances & Disease Registry, Association of Occupational and Environmental Clinics, SDS, OSHA, local health department, environmental agency, poison control

E: Educate: risk reduction, prevention, follow-up

NURSING INTERVENTIONS

PRIMARY PREVENTION

INDIVIDUAL: Educate individuals to reduce environmental hazards.

COMMUNITY
- Educate groups to reduce environmental hazards.
- Advocate for safe air and water.
- Support programs for waste reduction and recycling.
- Advocate for waste reduction and effective waste management.

SECONDARY PREVENTION

INDIVIDUAL
- Survey for health conditions that can be related to environmental and occupational exposures.
- Obtain environmental health histories of individuals.
- Monitor workers for levels of chemical exposures at job sites.
- Screen children 6 months to 5 years old for blood lead levels.

COMMUNITY
- Survey for health conditions that can be related to environmental and occupational exposures.
- Assess neighborhoods, schools, work sites, and the community for environmental hazards.

TERTIARY PREVENTION

INDIVIDUAL
- Refer homeowners to lead abatement resources.
- Educate clients who have asthma about environmental triggers.

COMMUNITY
- Become active in consumer and health-related organizations and legislation related to environmental health issues.
- Support cleanup of toxic waste sites and removal of other hazards.

Global health

- Health care delivery and health problems around the world affect the health of countries.
- Global health initiatives can be used to improve health status worldwide, and to promote equity in treatment.
- Health for All in the 21st Century (HFA21) outlines goals to promote productivity through adequate health care services around the globe.
- Examining the years of life lost from early death and disability provides information about the global burden of disease.

INFLUENCES ON GLOBAL HEALTH

- Wars and political unrest
- Natural and man-made disasters
- Limited resources and structure in lesser-developed nations
- International travel (increases spread of disease)
- Sanitation practices
- Climate change
- Maternal health
- Nutrition

GOALS FOR GLOBAL HEALTH

The United Nations created the Millennium Development Goals (MDGs) which called for more developed nations to contribute resources to improve conditions in lesser-developed countries, making global health a responsibility of nations around the world. In 2015, the goals were updated and replaced with a new list of Sustainable Development Goals. Qo1
- Eradicating hunger and extreme poverty
- Making primary education available worldwide
- Promoting empowerment of women and gender equality
- Promoting a sustainable use of ecosystems, including forests and oceans
- Developing global partnerships and promoting equality
- Promoting individual well-being and healthy lives
- Ensuring sustainable water, energy, and sanitation
- Promoting economic growth, industrialization, and innovation
- Making safe human settlements and cities
- Combating the effects of climate change
- Promoting peaceful, just societies

NURSING INTERVENTIONS

- Support the development of health care roles in countries that lack health care professionals.
- Promote the benefits of nursing as a distinct profession in health promotion and disease prevention and reducing health care costs.
- Work with governments and other developers of policy to promote the rights of nurses.
- Foster programs that promote environmental sustainability ("go green" campaigns to preserve natural resources, recycling facilities).
- Act as mentors or consultants to address the health of individuals and communities in other countries.

Access to and quality of health care

- The goal of a primary health care system is to make health care available in close proximity to people who need it, and to ensure that it be comprehensive with flexible cost to accommodate the income variations of the individuals who use those services.
- Community health nurses must advocate for improved access to health care services.
- Community health nurses can help shift the focus of the health care system from acute treatment of disease to primary prevention measures, in order to decrease health care costs and promote equity.

DATA COLLECTION

- Community assessment includes evaluating the adequacy of health services within the community and the accessibility of those services by those needing access.
  - Access to health care facilities and services
  - Adequate health care providers in general and specialty fields
  - Affordability of health services
  - Availability of medical benefits (through employers, free market, or government programs)
  - Barriers encountered by community members, especially vulnerable populations
- Inadequate health care insurance
- Inability to pay for health care services
- Health care illiteracy
- Language barriers
- Cultural barriers
- Lack of health care providers in a community
- Geographic isolation
- Social isolation
- Lack of communication tools (telephones)
- Lack of personal or public transportation to health care facilities
- Inconvenient hours
- Attitudes of health care personnel toward clients of low socioeconomic status or those with different cultural/ethnic backgrounds
- Eligibility requirements for state/federal assistance programs

ORGANIZATIONS AND FINANCING

Although providing health care is a human service, health care delivery is also a business, affected by economic influences. Good health status, in turn, positively affects the economy by increasing the individual's potential for productivity and wage-earning.

- **Microeconomic theory** examines individual preference and finances, and how those actions affect cost of care and resource distribution.
- **Macroeconomic theory** focuses on aggregate behaviors, economic growth, and employment.
- The cost associated with health care is a barrier to care for many. Some providers ration health care, and only offer services to individuals with certain coverage types.
- In the U.S., the government is involved in providing direct health care services, providing information and protection to the public, setting policies, and assisting providers and the public with finances.

ORGANIZATIONS

The health care system in the U.S. is influenced by federal and private organizations (insurers, employers), as well as global health organizations.

International health organizations

World Health Organization (WHO)
- Provides daily information regarding the occurrence of internationally important diseases
- Establishes world standards for antibiotics and vaccines
- Primarily focuses on the health care workforce and education, environment, sanitation, infectious diseases, maternal and child health, primary care

Federal health agencies

Veterans Health Administration
Finances health services for active and retired military persons and dependents (within the U.S. Department of Veterans Affairs)

U.S. Department of Health & Human Services
- Under the direction of the Secretary of Health
- Funded through federal taxes
- Consists of the following agencies:
  - **Administration for Children and Families (ACF)**
  - **Administration for Community Living (ACL)**: The ACL supports the needs of the aging and disabled populations and improves access to health care and long-term care services.
  - **Centers for Medicare and Medicaid Services (CMS)**: Also administers the Health Insurance Portability and Accountability Act (HIPAA), disability insurance, Aid to Families with Dependent Children (AFDC), and Supplemental Security Income (SSI)
  - **Agency for Healthcare Research and Quality (AHRQ)**: Conducts research to improve the quality, affordability, and safety of health care services. Uses research data to publish clinical guidelines and recommendations for a variety of health conditions. Qoi

- **Centers for Disease Control and Prevention (CDC):** Works to prevent and control disease, injury, and disability both nationally and internationally
- **Agency for Toxic Substances and Disease Registry (ATSDR):** Strives to decrease harmful exposure and diseases linked to toxic substances
- **Food and Drug Administration (FDA):** Works to ensure food safety as well as the safety and effectiveness of medications
- **Health Resources and Service Administration (HRSA):** Includes the Division of Nursing, Division of Medicine and Dentistry, and the Division of Public Health and Interdisciplinary Education
- **Indian Health Service (IHS):** Promotes tribal health for American Indians and Alaskan Natives
- **National Institutes of Health (NIH):** Supports biomedical research and includes the National Institute of Nursing Research
- **Substance Abuse and Mental Health Services Administration (SAMHSA):** Promotes behavioral health and aims to reduce the negative effects of substance use and mental illness

State health agencies

State departments of health: Obtain funding from state legislature and federal public health agencies

- Manages the **Women, Infants, and Children (WIC)** program, which promotes nutrition for women, infants, and children up to age five who are of low socioeconomic status
- Oversees **Children's Health Insurance Program (CHIP),** which offers expanded health coverage to uninsured children whose families do not qualify for Medicaid
- Establishes public health policies
- Provides assistance/support for local health departments
- Responsible for the administration of the Medicaid program
- Reports notifiable communicable diseases within the state to the CDC

State boards of nursing

- Development and oversight of the state's nurse practice act
- Licensure of registered and practical nurses
- Oversight of the state's schools of nursing

Local health department

Receives funds from the state level to implement community level programs

- The primary focus of a local health department is the health of its citizens.
- Local health departments offer various services and programs.
- Local health departments are responsible for identifying and intervening to meet the health needs of the local community.
- Local health departments work closely with local officials, businesses, and stakeholders.
- Local health departments report notifiable communicable diseases to state departments of health.
- Nurses at the community level typically function in the nursing roles of caregiver, advocate, case manager, referral source, counselor, educator, outreach worker, disease surveillance expert, community mobilizer, and disaster responder.
- Funded through local taxes with support from federal and state funds.

FINANCING

Financing for health care can come from a variety of sources, including individual payment, payment through organized insurance and health maintenance organizations, and public funding.

Affordable Care Act

- The Patient Protection and Affordable Care Act was created to help make health insurance affordable for all people and decrease the amount of federal spending on health care. It affects the way Medicare benefits are implemented and the way private insurance companies supply coverage.
- The full law is available through the U.S. Department of Health and Human Services website.

2.1 Medicare and Medicaid at a glance

Medicare

Individuals must be older than 65 years and receiving Social Security, have been receiving disability benefits for 2 years, have amyotrophic lateral sclerosis and receive disability benefits, or have kidney failure and be on maintenance dialysis or had a kidney transplant to qualify for Medicare.

Part A (hospital care, home care, hospice, limited skilled nursing care)

Part B (health care provider services, outpatient care, home health, diagnostic services, physiotherapy, durable medical equipment, ambulance service, mental health, preventive services)

Part C (also known as the Medicare Advantage plan: a combination of Part A and Part B and is provided through a private insurance company)

Part D (prescription medication coverage)

Medicaid

Medicaid provides health care coverage for individuals of low socioeconomic status and children, through the combined efforts of federal and state governments. Eligibility is based on household size and income, with priority given to children, pregnant women, and those who have a disability.

Medicaid provides inpatient and outpatient hospital care, laboratory and radiology services, home health care, vaccines for children, family planning, pregnancy-related care, and Early and Periodic Screening, Diagnosis, and Treatment (EPSDT) services for those younger than 21 years.

IMPORTANT ELEMENTS OF THE AFFORDABLE CARE ACT
- Extending eligibility for dependents to remain on parent's insurance until age 26.
- Prohibiting health plans from denying benefits for preexisting coverage to children under age 19.
- Banning lifetime limits on benefit coverage.
- Covering preventive care services.

Private funding

HEALTH INSURANCE

EMPLOYER BENEFITS

MANAGED CARE: based on using a case management approach with a specific group of providers in an attempt to contain the cost of care
- **Health maintenance organizations (HMOs):** Comprehensive care is provided to members by a set of designated providers.
- **Preferred provider organizations (PPOs):** Predetermined rates are set for services delivered to members; financial incentives are in place to promote use of PPO providers.
- **Medical savings accounts:** Untaxed money is put in an account for use for medical expenses.

Self-pay

Individuals are responsible for payment of charges not covered by a third party. Some clinics offer sliding-fee-scale payment where the rate of payment is based on the individual income.

NURSING INTERVENTIONS

- Use community assessment to identify barriers to adequate health care.
- Maintain awareness of health care standards and organizations that influence care delivery.
- Promote distributive justice in the use of health care resources.
- Understand the partnership and communication between local, state, and federal health entities. Qᴛᴄ
- Assist individuals and groups in obtaining adequate access to care, and work to promote equity in health care delivery.
- Maintain knowledge and skill related to economic principles, which can be applied to budgeting and funding of care.

Economic stability

Economic stability is related to the ability to access resources for life such as money, housing, food, and a job that provides a consistent living wage.

DATA COLLECTION

- Diverse and multiple job opportunities
- Availability of jobs with potential for advancement
- Salaries that cover the cost of living
- Thriving businesses with potential to attract more businesses

POVERTY AND HOMELESSNESS

- The federal poverty level is used to help determine which individuals can receive financial assistance (Medicaid, welfare).
- Individuals living in poverty are unable to pay for food, transportation, shelter, clothes, and medical care.
- Community regions that are characterized by poor housing, low employment rates, and increased rates of death and disease can be described as neighborhood poverty.
- Extreme poverty leads to inadequate housing and homelessness.
- Homeless individuals are those who do not have a regular nighttime residence and can include individuals who temporarily reside in a shelter, institution, or on the street.
- Incidence and prevalence counts can be used to number homeless individuals. The number is often inaccurate due to difficultly locating homeless individuals who can be transient, staying with friends, or residing in difficult-to-access locations.
- Health care for individuals who are impoverished or homeless is often only in times of acute exacerbation or crisis.

Poverty

CHARACTERISTICS OF INDIVIDUALS EXPERIENCING POVERTY
- Insufficient insurance coverage
- High-risk work and living environments
- Poor nutrition resulting from food insecurity
- Increased stress
- Less likely to engage in preventive activities or seek treatment for health problems
- Increased rate of chronic illness and accompanying physical limitations
- Increased morbidity and mortality rates

NURSING ACTIONS FOR PREVENTING POVERTY AND ASSISTING INDIVIDUALS LIVING IN POVERTY
- Coordinate free or low-cost health services and providers
- Coordinate collaboration with businesses and other employers to improve working conditions, benefits, and wages
- Teach health promotion and disease prevention
- Establish community partnerships that deliver culturally sensitive and competent services
- Collaborate with available resources that address housing insecurity

Homelessness

HOMELESS POPULATION CHARACTERISTICS
- Adults who are unemployed, earn low wages, or are migrant workers
- Female heads of households
- Families with children (fastest-growing segment)
- People who have a mental illness (large segment)
- Veterans
- People who have substance use disorders
- Unaccompanied youth
- Adolescent runaways (high incidence of lesbian, gay, bisexual, and transgender [LGBT] adolescents)
- Survivors of violence or neglect
- People who have HIV or AIDS
- Older adults who have no place to go and no support system ⓒ

HEALTH ISSUES OF HOMELESS POPULATIONS
- Upper respiratory disorders
- Tuberculosis
- Skin disorders (athlete's foot) and infestations (scabies, lice)
- Substance use disorders
- HIV/AIDS
- Trauma
- Mental health disorders
- Dental caries
- Hypothermia and heat-related illnesses from environmental exposure
- Malnutrition

NURSING ACTIONS FOR PREVENTING HOMELESSNESS AND ASSISTING INDIVIDUALS WHO ARE HOMELESS
- **Prevent individuals and families from becoming homeless** by assisting them in eliminating factors that can contribute to homelessness.
  - Refer those who have underlying mental health disorders to therapy and counseling.
  - Enhance parenting skills that can prevent young people from feeling the need to run away.
- **Alleviate existing homelessness** by making referrals for financial assistance, food supplements, and health services. Qⲧᴄ
  - Assist homeless clients in locating temporary shelter.
  - Assist clients in finding ways to meet long-term shelter needs.
  - If homeless shelters are not provided in the community, work with government officials to develop shelter programs.
- **Prevent recurrence of poverty, homelessness, and health problems** that result in conditions of poverty and homelessness.
  - Advocate and provide efforts toward political activity to provide needed services for people who have mental health disorders and are homeless.
  - Make referrals for employee assistance and educational programs to allow clients who are homeless to eliminate the factors contributing to their homelessness.

Rural residency

- Rural areas typically have less than 20,000 residents. Frontier areas have less than six persons per square mile.
- Urban areas typically have 20,000 to 49,999 residents, with larger central cities having a population of 1 million people or more.
- In general, low population densities are linked to decreased access to care, decreased health status, and decreased health-seeking behaviors.

HEALTH STATUS OF RURAL RESIDENTS
- Community health nurses who practice in rural settings often face challenges of limited resources and isolation from other providers. These nurses care for clients who have a broad range of conditions and are at ages across the lifespan.
- Higher infant and maternal morbidity rates
- Higher rates of diabetes mellitus
- Higher rates of obesity
- Less likely to meet physical activity recommendations
- Higher rates of suicide
- Increased trauma/injuries from lightning; farm machinery; drowning and boating; and snowmobile, all-terrain vehicle, and motorcycle crashes
- Increased occupational-associated risks (agriculture, fishing, mining, and construction are the most dangerous industries)
- Less likely to seek preventive care
- Increased risk for skin cancer from sun exposure
- Higher rates of respiratory complications from exposure to pesticides and chemicals
- Risk for stress-related health problems and poorer mental health

BARRIERS TO HEALTH CARE IN RURAL AREAS
- Distance from services
- Lack of personal/public transportation
- Unpredictable weather or travel conditions
- Inability to pay for care (underinsured/uninsured)
- Shortage of rural hospitals/health care providers

PRIORITY NEEDS FOR RURAL HEALTH
- Cancer prevention and care
- Mental health care
- Substance use prevention and treatment
- Immunization programs
- Family planning
- Food insecurity

NURSING ACTIONS FOR RURAL HEALTH
- Assist clients with identifying and applying for assistance programs.
- Use cultural competence when planning interventions.
- Establish trusting partnerships with key individuals in the community.
- Use existing relational ties between residents to foster community outreach initiatives.
- Teach prevention and protection measures for exposure to the elements and chemicals.

FOOD AND NUTRITION

Food security includes:
- Availability of food and nutrients
- Access to healthy food options
- Reliable sources of food

Food insecurity: limited access to affordable, nutritious foods
- In 2020 in the United States, 10.5 percent (13.8 million) households experienced food insecurity at some time during the year.
- For children, food insecurity affects physical development and ability to learn in school.
- Food insecurity affects the ability to manage chronic diseases (for example, hypertension, heart disease, obesity) and can lead to prolonged hospitalizations and delayed healing.

Higher rates of food insecurity occur in households:
- With incomes near or below the poverty line
- In which the head of the household is a single parent
- In which the head of the household is Black or Hispanic
- In large metropolitan areas

Social factors that may affect nutritional requirements and intake:
- Low literacy levels
- Language barriers
- Limited knowledge of nutrition and food safety
- Lack of social support
- Lack of or inadequate cooking supplies
- Limited or low income
- Limited access to transportation to obtain food
- Advanced age (older than 80 years)
- Lack of options for physical activity
- Use of tobacco or recreational drugs
- Limited use of or knowledge about community resources

Food deserts

- **Urban area:** community members live at least one-half mile from supermarket or grocery store. Food desserts may have stores and restaurants that provide high-calorie, low-cost foods with low nutritional value.
- **Rural area:** community members live more than 10 miles from a supermarket or grocery store

Healthy People 2030 objectives

- Reduce household food insecurity and hunger.
- Eliminate very low food security in children.

NURSING ACTIONS

- Identify food desserts, which limit access to affordable, nutritious foods.
- Establish partnerships with and provide referrals to organizations that address food insecurity:
  - Food banks
  - Meals on Wheels
  - Supplemental Nutrition Assistance Program (SNAP)
  - Special Supplemental Nutrition Program for Women, Infants, and Children (WIC)
  - National School Lunch Program
  - School Breakfast Program – designed to provide one-fourth of daily recommended level for key nutrients
    - Milk
    - Serving of fruit
    - Two servings of bread/cereal or meat/meat alternative (or a combination of bread and meat)

Access to and quality of education

Quality education gives individuals the chance to make a living wage, obtain health care benefits, make better health decisions, and live in zip codes with clean, safe neighborhoods and better access to goods and services.

Low levels of education are associated with poor health outcomes, higher levels of stress, and lower levels of self-confidence. Vulnerable populations are impacted more directly and disproportionately by low levels of education. Lasting consequences include decreased ability to secure a steady income that results from education.

DATA COLLECTION

- Quality education meets national standards and benchmarks for students
  - Strong retention and matriculation rates
  - Adequate supplies and competent educators
- Available, accessible, and affordable to the general public
  - Present in the local area or by virtual platform for class attendance
  - Low socioeconomic areas and rural areas may lack private or government funding for schools and internet access
- Helps shape the types of employment individuals can obtain
- Quality of education must meet needs of various employers who demand various skill sets
- Provides opportunities for preventive screenings for vision, hearing, obesity, and mental health issues
- Access to libraries

NURSING INTERVENTIONS

- Advocate for resources that have job training programs.
- Promote literacy programs.
- Promote community-based efforts to encourage diversity in hiring practices.
- Coordinate workshops for computer skills.
- Partner with schools to enhance cultural competency among educators.

Social and community context

- Access to programs that aid during times of crisis
- Support groups
- Neighborhood associations

Neighborhood and built environment

- Safe, clean, and accessible parks and public spaces
- Access to fresh food supplies within a two-mile radius
- Safe traffic patterns

Access to and quality of health care

- Affordable health care facilities and services
- Adequate health care providers in general and specialty fields of expertise
- Access to medical benefits (provided through employers or on the free market)

Economic stability

- Diverse and multiple job opportunities
- Salaries that can cover the cost of living for that area
- Thriving businesses with potential to attract more business

Food and nutrition

- Availability of food and nutrients
- Access to healthy food options
- Reliable sources of food

Access to and quality of education

- Schools with strong retention and matriculation rates
- Institutions of learning that have adequate supplies and culturally competent educators
- Access to libraries

Active Learning Scenario

A nurse is conducting an environmental health history during a postpartum home visit. Residents in the home include the mother, her partner, a 1-week-old infant, 2-year-old toddler, and 7-year-old child. Use the *ATI Active Learning Template: Basic Concept* to complete this item.

UNDERLYING PRINCIPLES

- Identify a Healthy People 2030 goal related to lead exposure.
- Identify a Healthy People 2030 goal related to safe water supply.

NURSING INTERVENTIONS: Using the I PREPARE mnemonic, assess environmental determinants of health for the residents in this house. Include two interventions in the Referrals and resources and Educate sections.

Active Learning Scenario Key

Using the ATI Active Learning Template: Basic Concept

Underlying Principles
- Healthy People goals
- Reduce exposure to lead in the population
- Increase the proportion of people whose water supply meets Safe Drinking Water Act regulations

NURSING INTERVENTIONS

Using the I PREPARE mnemonic:
- I - Investigate: Questions include potential exposure from peeling paint, and soil or water sources of toxins.
- P - Present work: Questions include place of employment, type of work, any personal protective equipment used, and any hazardous materials brought home from work on clothing.
- R – Residence: Questions include age of home, types of materials used in heating and plumbing equipment, recent remodeling, chemical storage, and water supply.
- E – Environmental concerns: Questions include quality of air and water in the community, industries in the neighborhood, and any nearby waste site or landfill.
- P – Past work: Questions include past jobs and any exposures.
- A – Activities: Questions include hobbies, recreation, gardening, fishing, hunting, use of pesticides, and alternative healing/medicines.
- R – Referrals and resources: Interventions include referral to the local health department for screening the children for lead exposure, referral to occupational health at places of employment for screening for chemical exposures, and referral to a local environmental agency for concerns about safe water in the home and recreational areas. Other resources include the Environmental Protection Agency, Agency for Toxic Substances & Disease Registry, Association of Occupational and Environmental Clinics, SDS, and OSHA.
- E – Education: Educational interventions include providing information about potential sources of lead exposure from toys, risks for waterborne illness from the local water supply, and local poison control resources.

Ⓝ *NCLEX® Connection: Safety and Infection Control, Accident/Error/Injury Prevention*

Application Exercises

1. A nurse is preparing an educational program on cultural perspectives in nursing. The nurse should include that which of the following actions by community members are influenced by social and cultural determinants of health? (Select all that apply.)

   A. Changing methods of preparing food

   B. Moving in with a parent to become their caregiver

   C. Seeking care from a medical provider when ill

   D. Family history of hypertension

   E. Asking a faith healer to cure a mental illness

2. A nurse is working on a plan for primary prevention within a community that has cultural practices which are unfamiliar to the nurse. Order the steps the nurse will take for the cultural assessment.

   A. Identify cultural factors that many influence the effectiveness of nursing actions

   B. Obtain an overview of cultural characteristics of the community.

   C. Organize data, including differences between the community's culture and Western medicine.

   D. Determine the perception the clients have about their current health practices

3. A nurse is conducting health screenings at a statewide health fair and identifies several clients who require referral to a provider. Which of the following statements by a client indicates a barrier to accessing health care?

   A. "I don't drive, and my son is only available to take me places in the mornings."

   B. "I can't take off during the day, and the local after-hours clinic is no longer in operation."

   C. "Only one doctor in my town is a designated provider by my health insurance."

   D. "I would like to schedule an appointment with the local doctor in my town who speaks Spanish and English."

4. A nurse is reviewing information about organizations that support community health efforts. Match each characteristic to the correct organization.

   A. Develop partnerships with community officials, businesses, and stakeholders

   B. License registered and practical nurses

   C. Manage the Women, Infants, and Children (WIC) program

   D. Includes the Agency for Healthcare Research and Quality (AHRQ)

   1. U.S. Department of Health & Human Services (USDHHS)

   2. State Departments of health

   3. State boards of nursing

   4. Local health departments

Application Exercises Key

1. A, B, C, E. **CORRECT:** When generating solutions for an educational program on cultural perspectives in nursing, the nurse should include nutritional practices, such as methods of preparing food; family structure, such as moving in with a parent; health care interactions, such as seeking care from a medical provider; and views about illness, such as asking a faith healer to cure mental illness as part of social and cultural context.

   (N) NCLEX® Connection: Psychosocial Integrity, Cultural Awareness/ Cultural Influence on Health

2. B, D, A, C

   When recognizing cues, the nurse should first perform a general assessment of community members' cultural characteristics, then seek information about current health practices, identify cultural factors that may influence the effectiveness of nursing actions, and organize the data that has been collected.

   (N) NCLEX® Connection: Psychosocial Integrity, Cultural Awareness/ Cultural Influence on Health

3. B. **CORRECT:** When analyzing cues, the nurse recognizes that the unavailability of providers during non-working hours is a barrier to accessing health care.

   (N) NCLEX® Connection: Psychosocial Integrity, Cultural Awareness/ Cultural Influence on Health

4. A, 4; B, 3; C, 2; D, 1

   When recognizing cues, the nurse should identify the USDHHS as the agency that includes the AHRQ. The nurse should identify state boards of nursing as the organizations responsible for licensing registered and practical nurses. The nurse should identify state departments of health as the organizations that implement maternal and child health programs, such as WIC. The nurse should identify local health departments as the organizations that develop community partnerships.

   (N) NCLEX® Connection: Management of Care, Legal Rights and Responsibilities

NCLEX® Connections

When reviewing the following chapter, keep in mind the relevant topics and tasks of the NCLEX outline, in particular:

Management of Care

PERFORMANCE IMPROVEMENT (QUALITY IMPROVEMENT): Utilize research and other references for performance improvement actions.

Safety and Infection Control

STANDARD PRECAUTIONS/TRANSMISSION-BASED PRECAUTIONS/ SURGICAL ASEPSIS: Apply principles of infection control.

Health Promotion and Maintenance

HEALTH PROMOTION/DISEASE PREVENTION: Assess and educate clients about health risks based on family, population, and/or community characteristics.

HIGH-RISK BEHAVIORS: Assess client lifestyle practice risks that may impact health.

CHAPTER 3

Epidemiology and Communicable Diseases

Epidemiology is used to monitor disease trends. Epidemiology draws from other disciplines and methods which include clinical medicine, laboratory sciences, social sciences, quantitative methods, and public policy. Examining numeric indicators of the occurrence of diseases or conditions, how long they last, and comparing that to historical trends assists with the management.

Worldwide, communicable diseases are responsible for the deaths of millions each year. Community health nurses must maintain knowledge of disease rates, modes of transmission, incubation, early manifestations, periods of communicability, and how to intervene at all levels of prevention related to communicable disease. Community health nurses utilize epidemiologic methods in their practice as they note trends in illness, and when they design, implement, and evaluate community health programs.

Understanding epidemiology and communicable disease facilitates individual and population prevention and treatment. It also helps with consideration of the burden of the disease, or how the number or prevalence of the disease will impact the health care structure and financial capability of the region, state, or nation.

Epidemiology

Epidemiology is the study of health-related trends in populations for the purposes of disease prevention, health maintenance, and health protection.

- Nurses use epidemiological principles to provide health interventions to targeted groups.
- Epidemiological calculations provide numerical information about the impact of disease and death on populations and aggregates.
- The epidemiological process is a systematic method of targeting a specific health need with the goal of improving health. Epidemiology provides a broad understanding of the spread, transmission, and incidence of disease and injury. This information is an important component of community assessment and program planning.
- Community health nurses are in the unique position of being able to identify cases and recognize patterns of disease, eliminate barriers to disease control, and provide education and counseling targeted at a disease condition or specific risk factors. Q͟ι

EPIDEMIOLOGICAL TRIANGLE
Epidemiology involves the study of the relationships among an agent, host, and environment (known as the epidemiological triangle). Their interaction determines the development and cessation of communicable diseases, as they form a web of causality, which increases or decreases the risk for disease.

- **The agent** is the physical, infectious, or chemical factor that causes the disease.
- **The host** is the living being that an agent or the environment influences.
- **The environment** is the setting or surrounding that sustains the host.

3.1 Epidemiological triangle

HOST

susceptible host
age   immunological status
sex   physiological state
genetics   occupation
ethnicity

chemical agents
drugs
toxins

physical agents
noise
temperature

infectious agents
viruses
bacteria

physical environment
geography
water/food supply
presence of reservoirs/vectors

social environment
access to health care
high-risk working conditions
poverty

AGENT

ENVIRONMENT

EPIDEMIOLOGICAL CALCULATIONS

Epidemiology relies on statistical evidence to determine the rate of spread of disease and the proportion of people affected. It also is used to evaluate the effectiveness of disease prevention and health promotion activities and to determine the extent to which goals are met.

INCIDENCE AND PREVALENCE RATES

Incidence and prevalence rates are used to measure the existence of a particular disease and allow the nurse to compare the rate of disease in one population to another, even though there can be different numbers of people in a given population.

> Incidence: Number of new cases in the population at a specific time ÷ population total x 1,000 = _____ per 1,000
>
> Prevalence: Number of existing cases in the population at a specific time ÷ population total x 1,000 = _____ per 1,000

MORTALITY RATES

Mortality rates provide information about cause of death. Public health workers can examine overall death rates (**crude mortality rate**), deaths from specific causes (**cause-specific rate, case fatality rate**), or deaths at specific times across the lifespan (**infant mortality ratio, age-specific rate**).

> Crude mortality rate: Number of deaths ÷ population total x 1,000 = _____ per 1,000
>
> Cause specific rate: Number of deaths from a specific cause ÷ population total x 1,000 = _____ per 1,000
>
> Case fatality rate: Number of deaths from a specific disease ÷ persons diagnosed with that disease
>
> Infant mortality rate: Number of infant deaths before 1 year of age in a year ÷ number of live births in the same year x 1,000 = _____ per 1,000

ATTACK RATE

A disease or condition is endemic when there is a moderate, ongoing occurrence in a given location.

Epidemic: Condition occurs when the rate of disease exceeds the usual (endemic) level of the condition in a defined population.

Pandemic: Condition occurs when an epidemic occurs in multiple countries or continents.

> Attack rate: Number of people exposed to a specific agent who develop the disease ÷ total number of people exposed.

Communicable diseases

- The degree to which an organism is able to cause a severe pathological reaction resulting in disease is referred to as the virulence, or degree of communicability.
- Individuals can be carriers of disease and not have the active infection.
- Leading causes of communicable disease deaths include acute lower respiratory infections (including pneumonia and influenza), HIV/AIDS, diarrheal diseases, tuberculosis, and malaria.
- Other diseases that pose a significant threat to community health include viral hepatitis and sexually transmitted infections. Further information about specific communicable diseases can be found in the **ADULT MEDICAL SURGICAL, MATERNAL NEWBORN, AND NURSING CARE OF CHILDREN REVIEW MODULES.**
- The Centers for Disease Control and Prevention (CDC) recommend routine immunizations according to age.
- Recommendations include schedules/guidelines for children, adolescents, and adults. A "catch up" schedule and recommendations for health care personnel are also available. The CDC website (www.cdc.gov) provides a high-quality resource for the most current information regarding immunization guidelines.

POPULATIONS AT RISK

- Young children
- Older adults
- Immunosuppressed clients
- Clients who have a high-risk lifestyle
- International travelers
- Health care workers

MODES OF TRANSMISSION

- Infectious diseases are transmitted either vertically, from parent to offspring, or horizontally through other person-to-person interactions. ⓆEBP
  - Vertical transmission occurs through the sperm, placenta, vaginal contact during birth, or consuming human milk.
  - Horizontal transmission occurs through contact with a person or objects the person has touched, the air, contaminated body fluids, food, and water (common vehicle), or living creatures like mosquitoes and snails (vectors).
- The Zika virus is an example of an infectious pathogen than can be transmitted vertically from mother to fetus or horizontally by contact with blood or secretions during sexual activity and by vector transmission through mosquito bite.

Airborne: particles transmitted by air to susceptible host via droplets or particles.
- Measles [airborne isolation precautions]
- Chickenpox [airborne isolation precautions]
- Tuberculosis (pulmonary or laryngeal) [airborne isolation precautions]
- COVID-19 [airborne isolation precautions]
- Pertussis [droplet isolation precautions]

- Influenza [droplet isolation precautions]
- Severe acute respiratory syndrome (SARS) [droplet isolation precautions]
- Common cold

Foodborne
- **Food infection** (bacterial, viral, parasitic infection of food)
  - Norovirus
  - Salmonellosis
  - Hepatitis A
  - Trichinosis
  - Escherichia coli (E. coli)
- **Food intoxication** (toxins produced through bacterial growth, chemical contamination, or disease-producing substances)
  - Staphylococcus aureus
  - Clostridium botulinum

Waterborne: fecal contamination of water
- Cholera
- Typhoid fever
- Bacillary dysentery
- Giardia lamblia

Vector-borne: via a carrier (vector), such as a mosquito, tick, fly
- West Nile virus
- Lyme disease
- Rocky Mountain spotted fever
- Malaria
- Zika Virus

Direct contact: transmission of infectious agent from infected host to susceptible host via direct contact
- Sexually transmitted infections: HIV/AIDS, chlamydia, gonorrhea, syphilis, human papilloma virus (HPV), genital herpes, hepatitis B, C, D
- Infectious mononucleosis
- Enterobiasis (pinworms)
- Impetigo
- Lice, scabies
- Common cold

DEFENSE MECHANISMS

Herd immunity: Protection due to the immunity of most community members making exposure unlikely

Natural immunity: Natural defense mechanisms of the body to resist specific antigens or toxins

Acquired immunity: Resistance acquired by the host through actual exposure to the infectious agent

Active: Production of antibodies by the body in response to infection or immunization with a specific antigen

Passive: Transfer of antibodies to the host either trans placentally from mother to newborn or through transfusions of immunoglobulins, plasma proteins, antitoxins

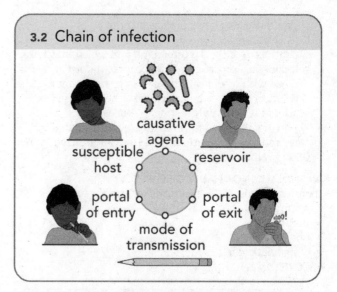

3.2 Chain of infection

causative agent
susceptible host
reservoir
portal of entry
portal of exit
mode of transmission

PREVENTION AND CONTROL Qs

- Prevention and control of communicable disease helps eliminate a disease from a specific location, or completely eradicates the existence of a particular disease. Refer to Fundamentals chapter 11 for general infection control principles.
- Nurses can create community programs that monitor individuals' adherence to treatment regimens to help minimize the spread of disease. This strategy also reduces the risk of complications for individuals, which can reduce the overall burden of disease on a community.
- Public health nurses can use the core functions to target communicable disease. For example, a nurse can identify cases of a disease (assessment), develop a program for city or county government to spray insecticide (policy development), and ensure proper follow-up for individuals who have tuberculin skin testing (assurance).

COMMUNICABLE DISEASE SURVEILLANCE

- The community health nurse engages in communicable disease surveillance, which includes the systematic collection and analysis of data regarding infectious diseases.
- Descriptive epidemiology is used to investigate disease patterns to identify whom it affected, where the issue is located, how it occurs, why or what the cause is, and when the condition started.
- Information gained from monitoring disease patterns can help identify an unusual disease outbreak or newly-emerging disease (public health assessment). The data is also useful in developing public health policies regarding disease management and to evaluate efficiency of communicable disease programs (assurance).
- Community health nurses can use disease surveillance to track the point of origin of some diseases. For example, the disease can be spread from a common individual or community (host), or a contaminated food or water source (environment).

- Surveillance also helps management of a disease outbreak.
  - Contract tracing is a intervention in which infected individuals report names and contact information for those with whom they have been in close contact. The contacts can then be informed of their exposure and offered testing and treatment, if necessary.
- Reporting of communicable diseases is mandated by state and local regulations, and state notification to the CDC is voluntary.

NATIONALLY NOTIFIABLE DISEASES
Identified at the CDC website and include the following. Qi
- Anthrax
- Botulism
- Cholera
- Congenital rubella syndrome (CRS)
- COVID-19
- Diphtheria
- Giardiasis
- Gonorrhea
- Hepatitis A, B, C
- HIV infection
- Influenza–associated pediatric mortality
- Legionellosis/Legionnaires' disease
- Lyme disease
- Malaria
- Meningococcal disease
- Mumps
- Pertussis (whooping cough)
- Poliomyelitis, paralytic
- Poliovirus infection, nonparalytic
- Rabies (human or animal)
- Rubella (German measles)
- Salmonellosis

3.3 Case study

Scenario introduction

A county public health department has received notification that multiple clients in a long-term care facility in a rural community near a large, metropolitan area have developed a communicable, airborne disease.

Ten cases of the disease were reported within the local community (population: 2,000) two weeks before the long-term care facility reported cases. Community health nurses had promoted the use of masks to prevent airborne transmission, but most of the community's residents were not regularly wearing masks in public spaces.

Scene 1

A community health nurse in the rural community is discussing their concerns with a supervisor at the health department.

Supervisor: "Is the facility requiring use of masks by clients, staff members, and visitors?"

Community health nurse: "The staff are using airborne precautions when caring for clients who have tested positive for the disease. I advised the director of the facility to require everyone in the facility to wear masks at all times, but only a small number of staff, clients, and visitors are doing that.

A big concern is that most of the staff positions are part time, so many staff members also work part time at multiple long-term care facilities in and around the city. Only a few are able to afford to own cars, so most use public transportation to commute between home and job locations."

Scene 2

Several weeks later, the incidence rate in the rural community is 10%, and the incidence in the city is 7%. The community health nurse and the supervisor at the public health department are discussing difficulties with contact tracing in the rural community.

Supervisor: "What kinds of barriers are you encountering that are making it difficult to conduct contact tracing?"

Community health nurse: "Most residents in the community live at or below the poverty line and do not have internet access or smart phones. They are not seeing information posted online about contact tracing and reporting symptoms. We leave a lot of voice mail messages when we call home phone numbers. About 20% of the population speak English as a second language. Some individuals have mentioned concerns about confidentiality because it is a small town. Some community residents are encouraging others to avoid reporting symptoms and avoid participating in contact tracing.

There is one primary care provider who is here three days a week, and their office is trying to help with contact tracing. A small number know the provider, though, because most families here do not have health insurance and have never met the provider."

Scene 3

The community health nurse is talking with a community health nurse in another nearby rural area.

Community health nurse 1: "The grocery store and most of the restaurants in this town are operating with limited hours because of staff shortages due to employees isolating because they tested positive for disease or quarantining because they have been in close contact with someone who tested positive. Also, supply issues have led to low levels of staples like milk, eggs, and bread."

Community health nurse 2: "That is the same in this community. There is a food bank in the city. Most of our residents do not drive, so they are dependent on the bus to get into the city, and if they are isolating or quarantining, they should not be using the bus."

Scenario conclusion

The nurses continue to plan additional actions they can take to support their communities.

Case Study Exercises

1. What are some other interventions related to SDOH that could be helpful in engaging community residents during this time?

2. What economic factors are social determinants of health for the long-term care facility staff that increase the risk for spread of this communicable disease?

3. List some social determinants of health in this community that increase the risk of disease transmission.

4. Name some community partnerships related to SDOH the community health nurses can explore when assisting community residents with obtaining basic supplies.

- Severe acute respiratory syndrome-associated coronavirus disease (SARS-CoV)
- Shigellosis
- Smallpox
- Syphilis
- Tetanus/C. tetani
- Toxic shock syndrome (TSS) (other than Streptococcal)
- Tuberculosis (TB)
- Typhoid fever
- Vancomycin-intermediate and vancomycin-resistant
- Viral hemorrhagic fever
- Staphylococcus aureus (VISA/VRSA)

HEALTH CARE GOALS

Regarding the control of communicable diseases

Reductions in
- Infections caused by pathogens often transmitted through food
- New HIV diagnoses among adolescents and adults
- New AIDS cases among adolescents and adults
- Number of perinatally acquired HIV and AIDS cases
- Deaths from HIV infection
- Sexually transmitted infections
- Health care-associated infections
- Vaccine-preventable diseases (reduction or elimination)
- Number of antibiotic courses for ear infections in young children

Increases in
- Consumers who follow food safety practices
- Surviving more than 3 years after a diagnosis of AIDS
- Adolescents and adults who have been tested for HIV in the past 12 months
- Testing for HIV in adults who have TB
- Substance use treatment facilities that offer HIV/AIDS education, counseling, and support
- Sexually active persons who use condoms
- Immunization rates among young children
- Immunization rates among adolescents
- Annual seasonal influenza immunizations among children and adults
- Adults who are immunized against pneumococcal disease
- Adults who are immunized against herpes zoster (shingles)
- Tuberculosis clients who complete therapy

IMMUNIZATION

- The community health nurse plays a major role in increasing immunization coverage to reduce the spread of vaccine-preventable diseases.
- Immunizations are often administered in community health settings, such as public health departments.
- The community health nurse often tracks immunization schedules of at-risk populations, such as children, older adults, immunosuppressed individuals, and health care workers.

- The community health nurse must educate the community about the importance of immunizations.
- The community health nurse must stay up to date on current immunization schedule recommendations and appropriate precautions when administering immunizations.
- The community health nurse understands that there are several barriers to obtaining immunizations: cost, vaccine delay or refusal, shortages, and changes in vaccine scheduling recommendations.

LEVELS OF PREVENTION

Primary prevention

- Prevent the occurrence of infectious disease.
- Educate the public regarding the need for immunizations, and federal and state immunization programs.
- Counsel clients traveling to other countries about protection from infectious diseases. Refer clients to the health department for information about mandatory immunizations.
- Educate the public regarding prevention of disease and ways to eliminate risk factors for exposure (hand hygiene, universal precautions, proper food handling and storage, use of insecticides, use of condoms).

Secondary prevention

- Increase early detection through screening and case finding.
- Refer suspected cases of communicable disease for diagnostic confirmation and epidemiologic reporting.
- Provide post-exposure prophylaxis (hepatitis A, rabies).
- Quarantine clients when necessary.
- Use partner notification and contact tracing to identify and screen individuals who have been exposed to a communicable disease. Qs

Tertiary prevention

- Decrease complications and disabilities due to infectious diseases through treatment and rehabilitation.
- Monitor treatment compliance, including directly observed therapy (DOT).
- Identify and link clients to needed community resources.

Active Learning Scenario

A nurse is reviewing the health department's communicable disease program. Use the ATI Active Learning Template: Basic Concept to complete this item.

UNDERLYING PRINCIPLES: Describe how primary, secondary, and tertiary prevention affects communicable disease.

NURSING INTERVENTIONS
- Include two primary prevention activities for communicable disease.
- Include two secondary prevention activities for communicable disease.
- Include two tertiary prevention activities for communicable disease.

Application Exercises

1. A nurse is preparing an education program on disease transmission for employees at a local day care facility. Sort each factor to the epidemiological triangle element in which the nurse should discuss it: Agent, Host, or Environment.

    A. Resource availability

    B. Ethnicity

    C. Toxins

    D. Bacteria

    E. Altered immunity

2. A nurse is planning measures to reduce the incidence of obesity. Which of the following interventions affects the environment, according to the epidemiological triangle?

    A. Determine whether clients have a family history of obesity.

    B. Measure clients' BMI.

    C. Provide low-fat meal options at public schools.

    D. Ask affected adults to keep a diary of food intake.

3. A nurse is reviewing data on the rates of varicella zoster (chicken pox) for a county. If there were 416 cases of varicella in one year among a population of 32,000 people, what should the nurse record as the incidence rate per 1,000 people? (Use whole numbers)

4. A nurse is determining the attack rate following an E. coli outbreak at a restaurant. If 84 people ate contaminated lettuce, and 13 people developed an E. coli infection, what should the nurse conclude as the attack rate?

Active Learning Scenario Key

Using the ATI Active Learning Template: Basic Concept

UNDERLYING PRINCIPLES

- Primary prevention: prevents the occurrence of communicable diseases.
- Secondary prevention provides screening for communicable diseases and minimizes spread to other individuals.
- Tertiary prevention decreases the complications from communicable diseases.

NURSING INTERVENTIONS

- Primary prevention
  - Teach about and provide immunizations.
  - Counsel clients on the risk of communicable disease when traveling outside the country.
  - Teach about proper hand hygiene.
  - Teach safe food preparation and storage techniques.
  - Teach about safe sexual contact.
- Secondary prevention
  - Refer clients suspected to have communicable disease for diagnostic testing and reporting.
  - Provide post-exposure treatment, if indicated, such as with rabies exposure.
  - Notify or recommend notification of the partners of infected clients, as indicated by legal guidelines.
- Tertiary prevention
  - Monitor clients prescribed medication for adherence to the treatment plan.
  - Assist clients who have impaired liver function following hepatitis with community resources.
  - Provide clients recovering with information about community resources such as transportation, food banks, and delivery programs.

Ⓝ *NCLEX® Connection: Safety and Infection Control, Standard Precautions/Transmission-Based Precautions/Surgical Asepsis*

Application Exercises Key

1. **AGENT**: C, D; **HOST**: B, E; **ENVIRONMENT**: A

    When generating solutions for an education program about disease transmission, the nurse should include toxins and bacteria as agents when discussing the epidemiological triangle. The nurse should discuss ethnicity and altered immunity as host factors when discussing the epidemiological triangle. The nurse should discuss resource availability as an environmental factor when discussing the epidemiological triangle.

    Ⓝ *NCLEX® Connection: Health Promotion and Maintenance, Health Promotion/Disease Prevention*

2. C. **CORRECT:** When generating solutions, providing low-fat meal options at public schools is an intervention that affects the environment of children and adolescents that may reduce the incidence of BMI greater than 30.

    A, B, D. Determining family history of BMI greater than 30, measuring clients' BMI, and encouraging a food diary are individual interventions for host factors and do not affect the environment.

    Ⓝ *NCLEX® Connection: Health Promotion and Maintenance, Health Promotion/Disease Prevention*

3. When analyzing cues about the data on the rates of varicella zoster for a county, the nurse calculates and reports an incidence rate of 13 cases per 1,000 people.

    \# cases/# population × 1,000 = incidence rate per 1,000 people

    416/32,000 × 1,000 = incidence rate per 1,000 people

    13 = incidence rate per 1,000 people

    Ⓝ *NCLEX® Connection: Management of Care, Performance Improvement (Quality Improvement)*

4. When analyzing cues about the attack rate following an E. coli outbreak, the nurse calculates an attack rate of 15 percent.

    \# exposed persons who developed infection divided by # exposed persons = attack rate

    13/84 = attack rate

    0.15 or 15% = attack rate

    Ⓝ *NCLEX® Connection: Management of Care, Performance Improvement (Quality Improvement)*

Case Study Exercises Key

1. When analyzing cues, the nurse should recognize that the need to work at multiple facilities and the need to use public transportation are economic factors that increase the risk for spreading a communicable disease.

    Ⓝ *NCLEX® Connection: Safety and Infection Control, Standard Precautions/Transmission–Based Precautions/Surgical Asepsis*

2. When analyzing cues, the nurse recognizes that factors related to economic stability, including poverty level, lack of health insurance, and rural residency, lead to less health-seeking behaviors and increase the risk of disease transmission. The nurse recognizes that factors related to health care access and quality, including language barriers and limited availability of primary care providers, increase the risk of disease transmission. The nurse recognizes that factors related to social and cultural context, including concerns about confidentiality and avoidance of contact tracing and reporting of symptoms, increase the risk of disease transmission.

    Ⓝ *NCLEX® Connection: Safety and Infection Control, Standard Precautions/Transmission–Based Precautions/Surgical Asepsis*

3. When generating solutions, the nurse recognizes that possible community partnerships include working with the food bank and other resources in the city to provide food distribution within the community, working with delivery services for delivery of food and other supplies, working with local churches to establish food pantries, asking for volunteers within the community to assist residents who are unable to obtain supplies.

    Ⓝ *NCLEX® Connection: Safety and Infection Control, Standard Precautions/Transmission–Based Precautions/Surgical Asepsis*

When reviewing the following chapter, keep in mind the relevant topics and tasks of the NCLEX outline, in particular:

Management of Care

COLLABORATION WITH MULTIDISCIPLINARY TEAM: Collaborate with interprofessional team members when providing client care.

CONTINUITY OF CARE: Follow up on unresolved issues regarding client care.

PERFORMANCE IMPROVEMENT (QUALITY IMPROVEMENT): Evaluate the impact of performance improvement measures on client care and resource utilization.

Health Promotion and Maintenance

HEALTH PROMOTION/DISEASE PREVENTION: Identify risk factors for disease/illness.

HIGH-RISK BEHAVIORS: Assess client lifestyle practice risks that may impact health.

Psychosocial Integrity

BEHAVIORAL INTERVENTIONS: Participate in group sessions.

CULTURAL AWARENESS/CULTURAL INFLUENCES ON HEALTH: Incorporate client cultural practices and beliefs when planning and providing care.

THERAPEUTIC ENVIRONMENT: Identify external factors that may interfere with client recovery.

Community Assessment, Education, and Program Planning

The role of the community health nurse in community health program planning and evaluation is a collaborative leadership role. The desired outcome is the improved health of the community through the role and functions of the community health nurse.

Community health nurses regularly provide health education in order to promote, maintain, and restore the health of populations. This is accomplished through a variety of means, such as community education programs.

The nurse can use program planning to promote healthy communities, in which community members partner with the nurse to address significant health issues.

Community health program planning should reflect the priorities set as a result of analysis of community assessment data. Priorities are established based on the extent of the problem (community members' perception of health needs, percent of population affected by the problem), the relevance of the problem to the public (degree of risk, economic loss), and the estimated effect of intervention (improvement of health outcome, adverse effects).

COMMUNITY HEALTH NURSE ROLES

The community health nurse is a key player in assessing the needs of the community.
- Interacting and establishing contracts with community partners serving the community at large
- Witnessing the interaction between community programs and the response of the client to the services
- Identifying future services based upon the visible needs of community members and population groups

COMMUNITY ASSESSMENT: INDIVIDUAL, FAMILY, AGGREGATES

- Community assessment is a comprehensive approach that emphasizes the community as a client, with the goal of providing benefit to the people of the area as a whole, rather than to individuals. Qᴘᴄᴄ
- Community assessment and diagnosis are the foundation for community-specific program planning.
- Using the nursing process, nurses can determine health needs within the community and assist in developing and implementing strategies to meet those needs. In doing this, it is necessary to expand the assessment, diagnosis, planning, intervention, and evaluation efforts from the individual to the community or aggregate level.
- To guide community interventions, nurses can conduct an assessment to identify the community's needs or strengths.
- Community assessment begins with defining the community to be studied. The community can be those in a share place (geographic community), those with a shared characteristic (demographic group), or with a common interest (functional community).

ECOLOGICAL MODEL

An ecological model for population health can be used as a guide to examine the determinants of health for a population, and for targeting interventions to multiple factors that affect health. It includes the following components.
- Individual traits (age, gender, biological, mental, and behavioral factors)
- Social, family, and community relationships
- Occupational and home environments
- Overall conditions created by local, state, national, and worldwide forces and trends

FACTORS TO CONSIDER

When determining the health of a community
- **Status:** Epidemiological data, client satisfaction, mental health, crime rates
- **Structure:** Presence of health care facilities, service types and patterns of use, demographic data
- **Process:** Relationships, communication, commitment to and participation in health

COMMUNITY ASSESSMENT COMPONENTS

People

Demographic: Distribution, mobility, density, census data

Biological factors: Health and disease status, genetics, race, age, gender, causes of death

Social factors: Occupation, activities, marital status, education, income, crime rates, recreation, industry

Cultural factors: Ethnohistory, ethnic groups, hierarchy and roles, language, religion and spirituality, values, customs, norms

Place or environment

Physical factors: Geography, terrain, type of community, location of health services, housing, animal control, business and industry, grocery stores

Environmental factors: Geography, climate, flora, fauna, topography, toxic substances, vectors, pollutants

Social systems

- Health systems
- Economic systems/factors
- Education systems
- Religious systems
- Welfare systems
- Political systems
- Recreation systems/factors
- Legal systems
- Communication systems/factors
- Transportation systems
- Resources and services

4.1 Steps for community assessment

1. define the community
2. collect data
3. analyze data (organize, review, prioritize)
4. establish community diagnoses
5. plan programs
6. implement programs
7. evaluate program interventions

DATA COLLECTION

Data collection is a critical community health nursing function. To best identify the health needs of the local community, it is essential to combine several methods of data collection. Relying on only one or two key pieces can result in an incomplete assessment.

Informant interviews

Direct discussion with community members or key informants for the purpose of obtaining information on local issues, strengths of the community, and concerns from their viewpoint.

STRENGTHS
- Minimal cost
- Participants serving as future supporters
- Offers insight into beliefs and attitudes of community members
- Reading/writing of participants not required
- Personal interaction can elicit more detailed responses

LIMITATIONS
- Built-in bias
- Meeting time and place

Community forum

Open public meeting

STRENGTHS
- Opportunity for community input
- Minimal cost

LIMITATIONS
- Difficulty finding a convenient time and place
- Potential to drift from the issue
- Challenging to get adequate participation
- Possibility that a less-vocal person can be reluctant to speak

Secondary data

Use of existing data (death, birth statistics; census data; mortality, morbidity data; health records; minutes from meetings; prior health surveys, determinants of health) to assess a problem

The nurse must evaluate the reliability of secondary data obtained from the Web. Generally, websites with .edu, .org, and .gov URLs present reliable information. ℚ⏎

STRENGTHS
- Database of prior concerns/needs of population
- Ability to trend health issues over time

LIMITATIONS
- Possibility that data might not represent current situation
- Can be time-consuming

Participant observation

Observation of formal or informal community activities

STRENGTHS: Indication of community priorities, environmental profile, and identification of power structures

LIMITATIONS
- Bias
- Time-consuming
- Inability to ask questions of participants

Focus groups

Directed talk (open ended questions) with a representative sample

STRENGTHS
- Possibility of participants being potential supporters
- Generates new ideas
- Provides insight into community support
- Reading/writing of participants not required

LIMITATIONS

- Possible discussion of irrelevant issues
- Challenging to get participants
- Requires strong facilitator
- Difficult to ensure that sample is truly representative of the overall community
- Time-consuming to transcribe discussion

Surveys

Specific questions asked in a written format

STRENGTHS: Data collected on client population and problems

- Random sampling
- Available as written or online format
- Contact with participants not required

LIMITATIONS

- Low response rate
- Expensive
- Time-consuming
- Possibility of collection of superficial data
- Requires reading/writing abilities of participants

Photovoice

Photo elicitation by community members to understand health issues from a community member's perspective

STRENGTHS

- Can be used with any community member including marginalized individuals
- Reading and writing not required
- Photography is an easy group activity

LIMITATIONS

- Cost associated with disposable cameras
- Some participants might not have access to a cell phone to take photos
- Time-consuming
- Photos might be lost

Windshield survey

A method of simple observation and a descriptive approach that assesses several community components by driving through a community

STRENGTHS: Provides a descriptive overview of a community

LIMITATIONS

- Need for a driver so the nurse can visualize and document the community elements
- Can be time-consuming
- Results based only on visualization and does not include input from community members
- Can be subjective

SURVEY COMPONENTS

- **People**
  - Who is on the street?
  - What is their general appearance (age, dress, well-nourished, malnourished, frail, unkempt)?
  - What are they doing?
  - What is the origin, ethnicity, or race of the people?
  - How are the different groups (subgroups) residentially located?
  - Is there any evidence of substance use, violence, disease, mental illness?
  - Are there any animals or pets in the community?
- **Place**
  - Boundaries
    - Where is the community located?
    - What are its boundaries?
    - Are there natural boundaries?
    - Are there man-made boundaries?
  - Location of health services
    - Where are the major health facilities located?
    - What health care facilities are necessary for the community but are not within the community?
  - Natural environment
    - Are there geographic features that can harm the community?
    - Are there plants or animals that could harm or threaten the health of the community?
    - What is the condition of the area?
  - Human-made environment
    - What industries are within the communities?
    - Could the environment or industry pose a threat to the health of community workers or the community itself?
    - Is there easy access to health care facilities?
    - Are the roads adequate and marked well?
    - What types of employment exist? Manufacturing? Retail? Small business? Military installation?
    - Are there grocery stores which provide fresh produce, or is this a "food desert"?
    - Where is garbage disposed? Is there evidence of trash, abandoned cars or houses?
- **Housing**
  - Is the housing of acceptable quality?
  - How old are the homes?
  - Are there single or multifamily dwellings?
  - Is the housing in good repair or disrepair?
  - Is there vacant housing?
- **Social systems**
  - Are there social services, clinics, hospitals, dentists, and health care providers available within the community?
  - Are there ample schools within the community? Are they in good repair or disrepair?
  - Are there parks or areas for recreation?
  - What places of worship are within the community?
  - What services are provided by local religious groups, schools, community centers, and activity or recreation centers?
  - Is there public transportation?
  - What grocery stores or other stores are within the community?
  - Is public protection evident (police, fire, emergency medical services, animal control)?
  - What indicators do you see about the politics of the community?

4.2 Case study

Scenario introduction

A local health department has identified increased incidence and prevalence of diabetes mellitus type 2 in a community. A health survey was conducted in the community 5 years ago. A new community health nurse is meeting with the director of a local community center to identify resources within the community and further explore the current needs of the community residents.

The community health nurse and director of the community center are talking at one of the tables in a large room with tables and chairs. The nurse is taking notes on their laptop during the meeting.

Scene 1

Nurse: "Thank you for meeting with me today. Because you serve so many residents of this community, I wanted to ask you a few questions about the needs and resources in the community. Is it okay if we get started?"

Director: "Yes. I hope we can find some ways to help more people."

Nurse: "What are the greatest needs you see in the community?"

Director: "Access to healthy foods, safe and reliable transportation, and primary care services."

Nurse: "Tell me about the resources for obtaining healthy foods."

Director: "The elementary school provides breakfast and lunch for students, and there is one grocery store, but it is not in the center of the community. There are a lot of fast-food restaurants. We used to hold a farmer's market at the center once a month, but the vendors lost interest, because not many people attended."

Scene 2

Nurse: "You mentioned that the grocery store is not in the center of the community. How do you think that impacts access of community members to healthy food choices?"

Director: "It is not within a walkable distance for many residents of the community. A lot of people here do not have their own cars, so they rely on bus transportation. One of the bus routes recently eliminated a few stops, and the buses on the other route do not stop as frequently as they used to."

Nurse: "What other options are there for obtaining food?"

Director: "There are some convenience stores around the neighborhood, and most of the food there is canned or boxed. The prices are higher than prices at the grocery store."

Scene 3

Nurse: "What types of access to health services do residents have?"

Director: "There is an urgent care clinic, and the grocery store has a clinic, but those clinics only take certain insurance plans. There used to be a community clinic in the center of the community, but it closed, so the nearest one is on the other side of town. We offer blood pressure checks and glucose screenings once a month here at the center. We have some volunteer nurses and doctors and pharmacists that do those. They usually have some educational materials to hand out, and they've offered some classes in the past about healthy eating and ways to stay healthy. Every fall, we have a flu vaccine clinic."

Nurse: "Will you share with me the average number of residents who participate in the blood pressure and glucose screenings, as well as the flu vaccine clinic?"

Director: "Yes, sure. I can send that to you later today."

Scenario conclusion

The nurse and director continue to talk for a few minutes, then the nurse closes their laptop. Nurse and director stand and shake hands. The nurse then conducts a windshield survey from the passenger seat of a car as someone else drives.

Case study exercises

1. Which of the following data collection methods is the nurse using during this meeting?

    A. Key informant interview

    B. Participant observation

    C. Focus group

    D. Health survey

2. After the meeting with the director of the community center, the nurse prepares to conduct a windshield survey of the community. Which of the following data should the nurse collect as a component of this assessment? (Select all that apply.)

    A. Location of health care facilities

    B. Individuals who hold power within the community

    C. Prevalence of disease

    D. Types of stores in the community

    E. Evidence of public transportation

3. Multiple methods of collecting data were named in this scenario. List the primary and secondary sources of data.

ANALYSIS OF COMMUNITY ASSESSMENT DATA

- The community health nurse plays an active role in assessment, data interpretation, and problem identification. Steps in analysis of community assessment data include the following.
  - Gathering collected data into a composite database
  - Assessing completeness of data
  - Identifying and generating missing data
  - Synthesizing data and identifying themes
  - Identifying community needs and problems
  - Identifying community strengths and resources
- Problem analysis is completed for each identified problem. Frequently, work groups are formed to examine individual problems and develop solutions. Q

COMMUNITY HEALTH DIAGNOSES

- Problems identified by community assessments are often stated as community health diagnoses.
- Community nursing diagnoses incorporate information from the community assessment, general nursing knowledge, and epidemiological concepts (especially the concept of risk in a population).
- Community nursing diagnoses often are written in the following format.

  Risk of [specific problem or risk in the community] **among** [the specific population that is affected by the problem or risk] **related to** [strengths and weaknesses in the community that influence the problem or risk].

> **Risk of** low birth weight **among** adolescents who are pregnant in the downtown district **related to** low income, lack of availability of nutritious food, and tobacco use as evidenced by lack of secure housing, food bank use, increased rates of unemployment, and smoking among pregnant adolescents.

COMMUNITY HEALTH EDUCATION

In designing community education programs, nurses must consider the barriers that make learning difficult. Some of these obstacles include age, cultural barriers, poor reading and comprehension skills, language barriers, barriers to access, and lack of motivation. Effective community health education requires planning. Qᴘᴄᴄ

LEARNING THEORIES

Behavioral theory: Use of reinforcement methods to change learners' behaviors

Cognitive theory: Use of sensory input and repetition to change learners' patterns of thought, thereby changing behaviors

Critical theory: Use of ongoing discussion and inquiry to increase learners' depth of knowledge, thereby changing thinking and behaviors

Developmental theory: Use of techniques specific to learners' developmental stages to determine readiness to learn, and to impart knowledge

Humanistic theory: Assists learners to grow by emphasizing emotions and relationships and believing that free choice will prompt actions that are in their own best interest

Social learning theory: Links information to beliefs and values to change or shift the learners' expectations

LEARNING STYLES

Community health nurses enhance the provision of education by addressing learning styles and domains of learning.

Visual learners: Learn through seeing and methods such as note-taking, video-viewing, and presentations. These learners "think in pictures."

Auditory learners: Learn through listening and methods such as verbal lectures, discussion, and reading aloud. These learners "interpret meaning while listening."

Tactile-kinesthetic learners: Learn through doing and methods such as trial and error, hands-on approaches, and return demonstration. These learners gain "meaning through exploration."

HEALTH LITERACY

Nurses should consider literacy needs when developing interventions. An individual's ability to understand basic health information and make decisions, or health literacy, can affect the ability or desire to take action.

DOMAINS OF LEARNING

Cognitive domain: Involves knowledge and the development of intellectual skills; for example, a client discusses how sodium intake will affect blood pressure.

Affective domain: Involves a change in attitude and development of values; for example, a client expresses acceptance of having a colostomy and maintains self-esteem.

Psychomotor domain: Involves the performance of a skill; for example, the community nurse teaches a client how to self-administer insulin.

DEVELOPMENT OF A COMMUNITY HEALTH EDUCATION PLAN

- First, identify population-specific learning needs. Qʟ
- Consider population-specific concerns and effects of health needs on the population to determine the priority learning need.
- Select aspects of learning theories (behavioral, cognitive, critical, developmental, humanistic, social learning) to use in the educational program based on the identified learning need.
- Identify barriers to learning and learning styles (visual, auditory, tactile-kinesthetic).
- Design the educational program.
  - Set short- and long-term learning objectives that are measurable and achievable.
  - Select an appropriate educational method based on learning objectives and assessment of participants' learning styles.
  - Ensure written educational materials are at a 5th grade or lower readability level.
  - Select content appropriate to learning objectives and allotted time frame.
  - Select an evaluation method that will provide feedback regarding achievement of short-term learning objectives and long-term impact on behavior.
- Implement the education program. Ensure an environment that is conducive to learning (minimal distractions, favorable to interaction, learner comfort, readability).
- Evaluate the achievement of learning objectives and the effectiveness of instruction.

COMMUNITY HEALTH PROGRAM PLANNING, DEVELOPMENT, AND MANAGEMENT

The planning step of community assessment leads to planning programs for the defined community. Within this planning step, the nursing process is repeated to establish and maintain the program.

Preplanning

Brainstorm ideas.
- Gain entry into the community and establish trust.
- Obtain community awareness, support, and involvement.
- Coordinate collaborations that have similar interests in addressing identified problems.

Assessment

Collect subjective and objective data about the community and its members.
- Complete a needs assessment and identify community strengths and weaknesses.
- Assess the availability of community resources.
- List potential sources for program funding (charitable giving, fund-raising, grants).
- Evaluate secondary health data.

Diagnosis

Identify and prioritize health needs of the community.
- Analyze data to determine health needs.
- Work with community members, local health professionals, and administrators to develop priorities and establish outcomes.
- In setting priorities among identified community problems, consider the following.
  - Community awareness of the problem
  - Community readiness to acknowledge and address the problem
  - Available expertise/fiscal resources
  - Severity of the problem
  - Amount of time needed for problem resolution

Planning

Develop interventions to meet identified outcomes.
- Determine possible solutions to meet the health need.
- Compare the resources and interventions required for each solution and select the best option.
- Establish goals and objectives for the selected solution.
  - Objectives are behaviorally stated, measurable, and include a target date for achievement.
- Select strategies/interventions to meet the objectives.
- Plan a logical sequence for interventions by establishing a timetable.
- Identify who will assume responsibility for each intervention. Qᴛᴄ
- Determine available and needed resources to implement interventions.
- Assess the personnel needed and any special training required for screening or providing education.
- Determine funding opportunities for needed interventions and develop a budget.
- Plan for program evaluation.

Implementation

Carry out the plan.
- Initiate interventions to achieve goals and objectives according to the program plan.
- Monitor the intervention process and the response of the community in terms of values, needs, and perceptions.

Evaluation

Examine the success of the interventions to determine if goals were met.
- Evaluate strengths and weaknesses of the program.
- Determine achievement of desired outcomes.
- Examine the adequacy, efficiency, appropriateness, and cost benefit of the program.
- Recommend and implement modifications to better meet the needs of the community.
- Share findings and recommendations with community members and stakeholders.
- Ongoing evaluation is necessary in order to ensure program success (sustainability) and meet the changing needs of the community.

STRATEGIES AND BARRIERS

HELPFUL STRATEGIES
- Thorough assessment
- Accurate interpretation of data
- Collaboration with community partners
- Effective outreach and communication patterns
- Sufficient resources
- Logical planning
- Skilled leadership

BARRIERS
- Inadequate assessment
- Inadequate or misconstrued data
- No involvement with community partners
- Impaired communication
- Inadequate resources
- Lack of planning
- Poor leadership

Active Learning Scenario

A nurse is planning a health promotion program for a community. The nurse collects the following data during community assessment.

- Curbside garbage pick-up
- Increased incidence of low infant birth weight
- Small amount of litter along the road
- Public transportation that operates 24 hr/day, 7 days/week
- Older playground equipment in need of repair
- High prevalence of diabetes mellitus
- Recreational trails that are in need of maintenance

Use the *ATI Active Learning Template: Basic Concept* to complete this item.

UNDERLYING PRINCIPLES: Identify possible ways the nurse might have obtained the data provided.

NURSING INTERVENTIONS
- Name one action the nurse should take as part of the diagnosis phase of program development.
- Name three actions the nurse should take as part of the planning phase of program development.

Application Exercises

1. A nurse is completing a needs assessment and beginning analysis of data. Place the actions the nurse will take in the correct order.

   A. Ensure data collection is complete.

   B. Determine health patterns within collected data.

   C. Identify health needs of the community.

   D. Compile collected data into a database.

2. A nurse is developing a community health education program for a group of clients who have a new diagnosis of diabetes mellitus. Which of the following learning strategies should the nurse include for clients who are auditory learners?

   A. Showing photographs of sites for injection

   B. Providing equipment to practice hands-on skills

   C. Supplying outlines for note-taking

   D. Facilitating small group discussions

3. A nurse is planning a community health program. Which of the following actions should the nurse include as part of the evaluation plan?

   A. Determine availability of resources to initiate the plan.

   B. Gain approval for the program from local leaders.

   C. Establish a timeline for implementation of interventions.

   D. Compare program impact to similar programs.

Active Learning Scenario Key

Using the ATI Active Learning Template: Basic Concept

UNDERLYING PRINCIPLES

- Curbside garbage pick-up: windshield survey, key informant interview, focus group
- Increased incidence of low infant birth weight: secondary data from health statistics
- Small amount of litter along the road: windshield survey
- Public transportation that operates 24 hr/day, 7 days/week: windshield survey, key informant interview
- Older playground equipment in need of repair: windshield survey, key informant interview, focus group
- High prevalence of diabetes mellitus: secondary data from health statistics
- Recreational trails that are in need of maintenance: windshield survey, key informant interview, focus group

NURSING INTERVENTIONS

Diagnosis phase

- Analyze collected data to determine health needs within the local community.
- Work with community members, local health professionals, and administrators to develop priorities and establish outcomes for identified health needs.

Planning phase

- Determine possible solutions to meet health needs of the community and select the best option.
- Establish goals and objectives for the selected solution.
- Select strategies/interventions to meet the objectives.
- Establish a timeline for implementation of interventions.
- Identify resources that are available, and resources that are needed, to implement strategies.
- Determine funding opportunities for needed interventions, and develop a budget.
- Plan for program evaluation.

Ⓝ *NCLEX® Connection: Health Promotion and Maintenance, Health Screening*

Case Study Exercises Key

1. A. **CORRECT:** When gathering information and recognizing cues about a community, informant interviews are direct conversations with individual community members for the purpose of obtaining ideas and opinions.

   Ⓝ *NCLEX® Connection: Health Promotion and Maintenance, Health Promotion/Disease Prevention*

2. A, D, E. **CORRECT:** When gathering information about a community and recognizing cues during a windshield survey, the nurse identifies the location of health care facilities, types of stores in the community, and evidence of public transportation.

   Ⓝ *NCLEX® Connection: Health Promotion and Maintenance, Health Promotion/Disease Prevention*

3. Informant interview, windshield survey, and community forum are examples of primary sources, because the nurse directly collects the data. Previous health survey results, attendance at screenings, and flu vaccine clinics are examples of secondary sources, because the nurse is reviewing data collected by someone else.

   Ⓝ *NCLEX® Connection: Health Promotion and Maintenance, Health Promotion/Disease Prevention*

Application Exercises Key

1. D, A, B, C

   In order to adequately and appropriately analyze cues from collected data, the nurse must first compile collected data into a database. From the data collected in the database, the nurse ensures that data collection is complete. The nurse then determines health patterns with the data and identifies the health needs of the community.

   Ⓝ *NCLEX® Connection: Health Promotion and Maintenance, Health Promotion/Disease Prevention*

2. D. **CORRECT:** Facilitating small group discussions provides an opportunity for clients who are auditory learners to learn as they listen to information. This is an appropriate strategy to include for this group.

   Ⓝ *NCLEX® Connection: Health Promotion and Maintenance, Health Promotion/Disease Prevention*

3. D. **CORRECT:** Include a comparison of program impact to similar programs as part of the evaluation plan. This comparison assists with determining the efficiency of the program.

   Ⓝ *NCLEX® Connection: Health Promotion and Maintenance, Health Promotion/Disease Prevention*

NCLEX® Connections

When reviewing the following chapter, keep in mind the relevant topics and tasks of the NCLEX outline, in particular:

Safety and Infection Control

ACCIDENT/ERROR/INJURY PREVENTION: Identify deficits that may impede client safety.

HOME SAFETY: Educate client on safety issues.

Health Promotion and Maintenance

DEVELOPMENTAL STAGES AND TRANSITIONS
Assist client to cope with life transitions.

Modify approaches to care in accordance with the client developmental stage.

HEALTH PROMOTION/DISEASE PREVENTION
Assess and teach clients about health risks based on family, population, and/or community characteristics.

Plan and/or participate in community health education.

Psychosocial Integrity

END-OF-LIFE CARE: Provide end-of-life care and education to clients.

FAMILY DYNAMICS: Evaluate resources available to assist family functioning.

RELIGIOUS AND SPIRITUAL INFLUENCES ON HEALTH: Assess psychosocial, spiritual, and/or occupational factors affecting care and plan interventions.

Practice Settings and Nursing Roles in the Community

Community health nurses practice in diverse settings. They practice as, public health nurses, home health nurses, hospice nurses, occupational health nurses, faith community nurses, school nurses, and forensic nurses.

Practice settings

PUBLIC HEALTH

Public health nurses are employed at federal, state, and local levels. The overall purpose of public health is to impact the health of populations through disease prevention, health promotion, and actions that protect population health.

Nurses working in public health support the 10 essential public health services:
- Monitoring community health and solving problems
- Diagnosing and investigating health risks
- Providing education and empowerment regarding health issues
- Facilitating community partnerships
- Developing community health plans and policies
- Enforcing health regulations
- Promoting equitable access to health care and services
- Assuring a competent diverse healthcare workforce
- Evaluating personal and population-based health services
- Researching solutions for health problems

Specific tasks the nurse might be engaged in include the following.
- Intervening to protect the natural environment
- Identifying problems for populations at risk
- Collecting vital statistics and analyzing the impact
- Providing specific health services to populations in alignment with laws and goals
- Managing communicable disease through prevention, screening, and treatment
- Scheduling wellness, screening, and immunization clinics
- Supervising and ensuring the competency of staff
- Legislating for policy implementation and revision
- Partnering with community health agencies
- Gathering statistics through surveillance, investigations, and monitoring vital statistics
- Fostering emergency preparedness

HOME HEALTH

Community health nurses provide health care services to clients where they reside. This includes traditional homes, assisted living facilities, and nursing homes.
- When making a visit to a client's home, the nurse should always take measures to ensure their own safety.
- The nurse is a guest in the client's home and should respect the values of the client and household members.
- Community health nursing care in the home setting is used to target specific at-risk individuals and groups.
- Community health nurses assist clients to transition from one level of care to another.
- Working as part of an interprofessional team is essential to providing holistic care. Q℠
  - The interprofessional team provides care for the client in the home and is comprised of nurses, physical therapists, occupational therapists, home health aides, social workers, dietitians, speech and language pathologists, respiratory therapists, psychologists, chaplains.
  - The primary care provider prescribes services that are then usually coordinated by the home health nurse.
  - The home health nurse functions as educator, provider of skilled nursing interventions, and coordinator of care. The nurse must consider the client assignment for each day and prioritize the order of visits. Critical thinking skills are essential in this setting since there is so much autonomy.
  - Many clients leave the hospital in just a few days and are still very ill.
  - These clients and their family members need skilled services and education about the disease process, prescribed medications, and future implications of their illnesses.

SKILLED SERVICES INCLUDE:
- Skilled assessment
- Wound care
- Laboratory draws
- Medication education and administration
- Infection prevention
- Parenteral nutrition
- IV fluids and medication
- Central line care
- Urinary catheter insertion and maintenance
- Coordination, delegation, and supervision of various other participants in health services

Omaha System model

Nurses caring for individuals, families, and communities under home health and hospice care often use the Omaha System model to implement the nursing process. The framework is also used in many electronic health record systems.

STEPS OF THE OMAHA SYSTEM Qℓ
- Collecting and assessing data
- Stating the problem
- Identifying an admission problem rating using a problem classification scheme
- Planning and intervening
- Re-rating problems during the span of care delivery and at discharge
- Evaluating the end problem outcome

LIVING ENVIRONMENT

The home health nurse must evaluate the living environment for safety, paying close attention to nonsecure rugs, electrical outlets, and extension cords; the use of oxygen; low lighting; the need for safety devices in the bathroom; and other potential environmental hazards. Qs

> Older adults are at a particular risk for falls.

QUESTIONS TO ASK
- Does the client have food in the house to eat?
- Is there help with household activities?
- Does the client live alone?
- Who is the client's support system?
- Is the client able to set up and dispense their own medication?
- Does the client have access to health care?

CLIENT EDUCATION

Home health nurses provide follow-up care after an acute hospital stay. They must educate the client and the family regarding complications or adverse reactions.
- These instructions can include when to contact the agency, emergency room, or provider.
- Information and resources for families and clients can provide support in dealing with illness.

Providing education encourages clients to be independent and involved in their own care. It also allows families to be involved in the care and decision-making regarding their family members.

HOSPICE

Hospice care focuses on enhancing the quality of life through the provision of palliative care, supporting the client and family or friends through the dying process, and providing bereavement support to the family following the client's death.
- Clients can receive hospice care in a variety of settings, including the home, hospice centers, hospitals, and long-term care settings.
- Hospice care is a comprehensive care delivery system for clients who are terminally ill. Further medical care aimed toward a cure is stopped. The focus becomes relief of pain and suffering, as well as enhancing quality of life.
- The hospice nurse provides care for the client and the client's entire family. Hospice care includes skilled, direct services and indirect care coordination. Qpcc
- Hospice care uses an interprofessional approach.
- Controlling manifestations of the medical problem and dying process is a priority.
- The provider directs hospice care services, which are then managed by the nurse.
- Volunteers are used for nonmedical care.
- Postmortem bereavement services are offered for the family.
- Helping the family transition from an expectation of recovery to acceptance of death is an important aspect of providing hospice care.

OCCUPATIONAL HEALTH

All work environments have associated risks. Health care in the workplace seeks to both promote health and prevent occupational illness and injury. Through improvement and maintenance of health, workplace expenditures are decreased by less sick time use, fewer workers' compensation claims, and decreased use of group health coverage.
- Nurses function in numerous roles within workplace settings and are challenged to provide cost-effective and high-quality care. In this effort, it is essential for the occupational health nurse to develop partnerships with workplace administration, industrial hygienists, safety specialists, ergonomists, occupational medicine physicians, human resource departments, union representatives, and health insurance agencies. Qtc
- The occupational health nurse works to promote a healthy work environment to foster the health and safety of workers. Qs
  - Assessing risks for work-related illness and injury
  - Planning and delivering health and safety services in the workplace
  - Collaborating with community health care providers
  - Facilitating health promotion activities that lead to a more productive workforce
- This autonomous specialty entails making independent nursing judgments when providing care to the workforce aggregate.

SUSCEPTIBILITY

In assessing risk for work-related illness and injury, the nurse should keep in mind the following factors affecting susceptibility to illness and injury.

HOST FACTORS: Worker characteristics (job inexperience, age, pregnancy, sex, health status, work practices, ethnicity, and lifestyle factors)

AGENT FACTORS
- Biological agents: viruses, bacteria, fungi, blood-borne, airborne pathogens
- Chemical agents: asbestos, smoke, lead, mercury, cadmium, nickel, zinc, and antineoplastic drugs
- Enviromechanical agents: musculoskeletal or other strains from repetitive motions, poor workstation-worker fit, lifting heavy loads, slippery floors, cluttered work areas
- Physical agents: temperature extremes, vibrations, noise, radiation, lighting
- Psychosocial agents: threats to psychological or social well-being resulting in work-related stress, burnout, violence, interpersonal relationships

ENVIRONMENTAL FACTORS
- Physical factors: heat, odor, ventilation, pollution
- Social factors: sanitation, overcrowding
- Psychological factors: addictions, stress

RESPONSIBILITIES

Occupational health nurses' roles and responsibilities include the following.

Primary prevention: Teaching good nutrition and knowledge of health hazards, and providing information on immunizations and use of protective equipment

Secondary prevention: Identifying workplace hazards, early detection through health surveillance and screening, prompt treatment, counseling and referral, and prevention of further limitations

Tertiary prevention: Restoration of health through rehabilitation strategies and limited-duty programs

EXPOSURE TO HAZARDS

An occupational health history provides the framework for a nurse to begin to assess a worker for possible exposure to health hazards.

- The goal is to identify agents and host factors that place the worker at risk, identify ways to eliminate or minimize exposure, and prevent potential health problems.
- Information elicited should include the following.
  - Current and past jobs
  - Current and past exposure to specific agents and any relationship of current manifestations to work activities
  - Any precipitating factors (underlying illness, previous injuries, healthy or unhealthy habits)

SITE WALK-THROUGH

A work site walk-through or survey is also part of a workplace assessment. The occupational health nurse should focus on the following.

- Observation of work processes and materials
- Job requirements
- Actual and potential hazards
- Employee work practices (hygiene, waste disposal, housekeeping)
- Incidence/prevalence of work-related illness/injuries
- Control strategies to eliminate exposures

CONTROL STRATEGIES

Control strategies are designed to reduce future exposures based upon results from investigations into work-related illness/injury. Control strategies often include the following.

- Engineering
- Altering work practices
- Providing personal protective equipment and education to prevent future injuries
- Workplace monitoring
- Health screening
- Employee-assistance programs
- Job-task analysis
- Design, risk management, and emergency preparedness

PROTECTION

From violence

- Work can be frustrating and contribute to stress, resulting in aggression and violence against others.
- Identify jobs that are repetitive, boring, or physically and psychologically draining, which can help to identify workers who might feel tired, angry, and generally inadequate.
- Nurses can refer such workers to employee-assistance programs that provide confidential counseling and referrals to other professional services if needed.

From work-related injuries

Related to falls, environmental hazards, and burns. Nurses can use research and trend analysis to improve working conditions by eliminating or minimizing hazards and potential problems. Q EBP

ADDITIONAL STRATEGIES

- Provide safety and health education programs to workers.
- Develop health policy focused on ensuring effective employee health and safety.
- Design strategies to prevent work-related accidents/injuries.
- Keeping abreast of Occupational Health and Safety Administration (OSHA) standards and resource programs.
- Working to influence legislation aimed at workers/workplace health protection.

OCCUPATIONAL HEALTH AND LEGISLATION

Occupational Safety and Health Act of 1970

Occupational Health and Safety Administration (OSHA): Develops and enforces workplace health regulations to protect the safety and health of workers. Provides education to employers about workplace health and safety.

National Institute for Occupational Safety and Health (NIOSH): A part of the Centers for Disease Control and prevention, it focuses on identification of workplace hazards and research for prevention of work-related injury and illness. Provides education to safety and health professionals about workplace safety.

National Advisory Committee on Occupational Safety and Health (NACOSH): The advisory committee is made up of 12 members representing labor, occupational health, safety professions, and the general public. The committee's purpose is to advise the secretaries of labor and health and human services on policies and programs that affect occupational safety and health.

Workers' compensation acts

State-level legislation that regulates financial compensation to workers suffering from injuries or illness resulting from the workplace.

FAITH COMMUNITY

The faith community nurse works with individuals, families, and faith communities who share common faith traditions. Most religions have practices that are important to health and healing, and many follow specific practices when caring for an ill or dying member.

- Members of faith communities (congregants) represent the entire lifespan and all family types. This offers nurses the opportunity to work with a diverse population within the same setting.
- Faith community nurses provide interventions to individuals and groups in homes, congregational meeting places, acute or long-term care facilities, or through schools.
- The practice of faith community nursing is governed by each state's nurse practice act and standards of practice.
- Nursing interventions are based on spiritual, physical, emotional, and social dimensions.
- Faith community nurses must be aware of faith and belief practices of the congregants served. Caring and spirituality are central among faith-based organizations.

FICA SPIRITUALITY ASSESSMENT TOOL Qᴾᶜᶜ
- **F:** Faith or belief
- **I:** Importance or influence
- **C:** Community
- **A:** Address (interventions to address)

Missionary nurse

Missionary nursing seeks to promote health and prevent disease by meeting spiritual, physical, and emotional needs of people across the globe. These nurses can be career missionaries, or can serve as short-term, volunteer, or part-time missionaries.

Cultural and language barriers often affect the provision of care. Collaboration within the community is essential in meeting goals.

Faith community nurse

Faith community nurses , previously called parish nurses, promote the health and wellness of populations of faith communities. The population often includes church members, individuals, families, and groups in the geographical community.

Faith community nurses work closely with pastoral care staff, professional health care members, and lay volunteers to provide a holistic approach to healing (body, mind, and spirit). Qᵀᶜ

FUNCTIONS OF THE FAITH COMMUNITY NURSE
- Personal health counseling (health-risk appraisals, spiritual assessments, support for numerous acute and chronic, actual and potential health problems)
- Health education (available resources, classes, individual and group teaching)
- Liaison between faith community and local resources
- Facilitating support groups
- Spiritual support (help identify spiritual strengths for coping)

SCHOOL

School nursing encompasses many roles.

Case manager: Coordinates comprehensive services for children who have complex health needs.

Community outreach: Strives to meet the needs of all school-age children by cooperative planning and collaboration between the educational system and other community agencies.

Consultant: Assists students, families, and personnel in information gathering and decision-making about a variety of health needs and resources.

Counselor: Supports students on a wide variety of health needs. Can provide grief counseling.

Direct caregiver: Provides nursing care to ill or injured children at school.

Health educator: Helps prepare children, families, school personnel, and the community to make well-informed health decisions.

Researcher: Contributes to the base of knowledge for school health and educational needs. Q�قᴵ

LEVELS OF PREVENTION

Primary prevention

Assess the knowledge base regarding health issues.
Teach health promotion practices.
- Hand hygiene and tooth-brushing
- Healthy food choices
- Injury prevention, including seat belt use and bike, fire and water safety
- Substance use prevention
- Immunizations
- Disease prevention

Assess the immunization status of all children: Maintain current records of required immunizations.

Secondary prevention

Assess children who become ill or injured at school.
Provide care to children who have the following.
- Headaches
- Stomach pain, diarrhea
- Anxiety over being separated from parents
- Minor injuries (cuts or bruises) that occur at school

Assess all children, faculty, and staff during emergencies.
- Provide emergency care (first aid, early defibrillation with AED, CPR).
- Create emergency plans for children who have a potential for anaphylactic reactions or other health problems that could result in an emergency situation.
- Maintain inventory of emergency supply equipment and secure medications.

Perform screening for early detection of disease and initiate referrals as appropriate.
- Vision and hearing
- Height and weight
- Oral health
- Scoliosis
- Infestations (lice)
- General physical examinations

Assess children to detect child abuse or neglect.
The school nurse is required by state law to officially report all suspected cases of child abuse/neglect.

Assess children for evidence of mental illness, suicide, and violence.
Identify children at risk.

Respond to school crises and disasters.
- Develop a crisis plan.
- Act as a first responder or triage the injured.
- Participate in drills.
- Counsel and debrief.

Tertiary prevention

Assess children who have disabilities.
- Participate in developing the individual education plan (IEP) for children who have disabilities.
- Work with child/family to develop and achieve long-term outcomes.

Assess children who have long-term health needs at school.

Provide nursing care for children who have chronic disorders, including asthma, diabetes mellitus, and cystic fibrosis.
Administer medication per provider's prescription.
- The prescribed medication should be in the original bottle and stored in a secure place.
- Written consent by the parents for medication administration is required.
- Provide care to children who have specific health needs, including the following.
  ○ Urinary catheterizations
  ○ Dressing changes
  ○ IV line monitoring/medication administration
  ○ Tracheostomy suctioning
  ○ Tube feeding administration

Provide ongoing care for adolescent parents or adolescents who are pregnant.
- Assist in pregnancy identification.
- Provide parenting education.
- Educate adolescents on prevention of future pregnancies.

COMPONENTS OF COORDINATED SCHOOL HEALTH PROGRAMS

Health education: Inclusion of health concepts in courses of study for children in pre-K through grade 12

Physical education: Promoting physical activity in school

Health services: Providing health services in school by qualified professionals (nurses, physicians, dentists, allied health professionals)

Nutrition services: Providing access to meals that accommodate the health and nutrition needs of all children

Counseling, psychological, and social services: Providing services that improve the mental, emotional, and social health of students, as well as the overall school

Promotion of a healthy and safe school environment: Reducing illicit drug and tobacco use and violence in schools

Health promotion for staff: Promoting activities that encourage health promotion and disease prevention behaviors among the school's faculty and staff

Facilitation of family/community involvement: Promoting collaboration between the school, parents/caregivers, community resources

Facilitating safety policies: Assisting with the development of policies and procedures for staff in the event of fire, disaster, or injury. This is particularly important for schools where the nurse is not present full-time.

5.1 Examples of levels of prevention

Primary
- School nurse places hand hygiene posters near restrooms
- Forensic nurse develops a program to prevent infant suffocation

Secondary
- School nurse screens for pediculosis
- Faith community nurse identifies safety concerns during a home visit

Tertiary
- Faith community nurse assists a congregant to obtain tube feeding supplies
- Home health nurse refers a client with a chronic illness for palliative care

FORENSICS

Injury is a common cause of altered health that is preventable. Reducing the incidence of injury and promoting recovery reduces the financial burden of the condition. Qs

Forensic nurses care for perpetrators of injury as well as victims of sexual assault, substance use related injuries, human trafficking, physical abuse, gang violence, disaster, and accidental injuries.

- Forensic nursing combines nursing knowledge with knowledge of the criminal justice system, and epidemiological knowledge about findings of intentional injury.
- Forensic nurses work in a variety of settings, including clinics, emergency departments, law enforcement agencies, mental health facilities, and correctional facilities.
- Safety is the primary principle of forensic nursing care. Other key principles include respect, beneficence, nonmaleficence, caring, justice, truth, and the use of intuition.
- Many forensic nursing roles require advanced education and certification. Credentialing in forensic nursing is available for the sexual assault nurse examiner (SANE) and advanced practice forensic nurses.
- The SANE collects detailed medical, physical, and emotional data from clients following a sexual assault, manages samples, and provides support to clients. A SANE often testifies in legal proceedings related to findings of client assessment.

LEVELS OF PREVENTION

Primary prevention: Develop and implement injury prevention programs (sudden unexpected infant death [SUID], sexual assault).

Secondary prevention

- Examine victims of crime for indicators of intentional injury.
- Provide direct care to both the client following a sexual assault and perpetrator.
- Collect and preserve evidence from possible crimes, using written and picture documentation.

Tertiary prevention

- Provide treatment to incarcerated individuals.
- Liaison between clients following trauma, medical care facilities, and the legal community to minimize the burden of trauma on the client.
- Connect clients with community resources after injury (mental health counseling, physical rehabilitation).

Application Exercises

1. A nurse is speaking with a client who asks for additional information about hospice. Which of the following statements should the nurse make?
   A. "Clients who require skilled nursing care at home qualify for hospice care."
   B. "One function of hospice is to provide teaching to clients about life-sustaining measures."
   C. "Hospice assists clients to develop the skills needed to care for themselves independently."
   D. "A component of hospice care is to control the client's manifestations."

2. An occupational health nurse at a local industrial facility is discussing factors that affect risk for work-related illness and injury. Identify the following factors as physical, psychological, or mechanical.
   A. Noise
   B. Heavy lifting
   C. Poor lighting
   D. Repetitive motion
   E. Stress
   F. Violence

3. A newly hired occupational health nurse at an industrial facility is performing an initial workplace assessment. Which of the following information should the nurse determine when conducting a work site survey?
   A. Work practices of employees
   B. Past exposure to specific agents
   C. Past jobs of individual employees
   D. Length of time working in current role

4. A school nurse is scheduling visits with a physical therapist for a child who has cerebral palsy. In which of the following roles is the nurse functioning?
   A. Direct caregiver
   B. Consultant
   C. Case manager
   D. Counselor

Active Learning Scenario

A school nurse is planning prevention activities for students. Use the *ATI Active Learning Template: Basic Concept* to complete this item.

RELATED CONTENT

- Define primary prevention.
- Define secondary prevention.
- Define tertiary prevention.

NURSING INTERVENTIONS

- Include two primary prevention activities the nurse should plan.
- Include two secondary prevention activities the nurse should plan.
- Include two tertiary prevention activities the nurse should plan.

Active Learning Scenario Key

Using the ATI Active Learning Template: Basic Concept

RELATED CONTENT

- Primary prevention: Strategies that prevent the initial occurrence of disease or injury
- Secondary prevention: Strategies that lead to early detection and treatment of disease with the goal of limiting severity and adverse effects
- Tertiary prevention: Strategies that maximize recovery after an injury or illness

NURSING INTERVENTIONS

Primary prevention activities

- Teaching healthy heart curriculum (nutrition, exercise, not smoking)
- Educating about dental health
- Discussing safety (seat belts, bicycle helmets, stranger safety)
- Administering immunizations
- Teaching about communicable disease transmission
- Providing sex education
- Advocating for safe playground equipment
- Providing substance use prevention education

Secondary prevention activities

- Performing tuberculin skin tests
- Performing routine checks for pediculosis
- Taking measures to control communicable disease outbreaks
- Screening for lead exposure
- Implementing scoliosis screenings
- Identifying students at risk for suicide or self-harm
- Performing vision and hearing screenings
- Measuring heights and weights
- Identifying indicators of child abuse or neglect

Tertiary prevention activities

- Teaching about allergic triggers for students who have asthma
- Administering medications to treat chronic conditions (asthma, attention deficit hyperactivity disorder, seizure disorders)
- Monitoring glucose levels and administering insulin to students who have diabetes mellitus
- Discussing and planning for nutritional needs of students who have cystic fibrosis
- Developing communication methods for students who have autism spectrum disorders

Ⓝ *NCLEX® Connection: Health Promotion and Maintenance, Health Promotion/Disease Prevention*

Application Exercises Key

1. D. **CORRECT:** Controlling the client's manifestations of medical problems or the dying process and improving quality of life are components of hospice care.

Ⓝ *NCLEX® Connection: Basic Care and Comfort, Nonpharmacological Comfort Interventions*

2. **PHYSICAL:** A, C; **PSYCHOLOGICAL:** E, F; **MECHANICAL:** B, D

   When taking the action of discussing risks for work-related illness and injury, the nurse should discuss factors of noise and lighting as physical agents. The nurse should discuss factors of stress and violence as psychosocial l agents. The nurse should discuss repetitive motion and heavy lifting as mechanical factors.

Ⓝ *NCLEX® Connection: Basic Care and Comfort, Psychosocial Integrity, Stress Management*

3. A. **CORRECT:** Determine the work practices of employees when conducting a work site survey.

Ⓝ *NCLEX® Connection: Health Promotion and Maintenance, Health Promotion/Disease Prevention*

4. C. **CORRECT:** In the role of case manager, a school nurse coordinates comprehensive services for students who have complex health needs.

Ⓝ *NCLEX® Connection: Management of Care, Case Management*

NCLEX® Connections

When reviewing the following chapter, keep in mind the relevant topics and tasks of the NCLEX outline, in particular:

Management of Care

ADVOCACY: Act in the role of client advocate.

CASE MANAGEMENT: Plan individualized care for client based on need.

Health Promotion and Maintenance

HEALTH PROMOTION/DISEASE PREVENTION: Plan and/or participate in community health education.

HEALTH SCREENING: Perform health history/health and risk assessments.

CHAPTER 6 *Aggregates in the Community*

Aggregates are groups that have a common characteristic. Aggregates or target populations can be defined based on special interests or geographic locations. Identify aggregates when planning targeted health interventions.

Aggregates receive services from community health nurses. These include individuals from infancy to death, families, and groups within the community.

Children (birth to 12 years) and adolescents

The income level of caregivers affects the children in many ways. Children living in families who have low-income status can face low food security, are at risk for homelessness, and might have difficulty learning and developing cognitively. **SDoH**

Access to care is another concern for children. Legislation, such as the Affordable Care Act, and programs like Medicaid and the Children's Health Insurance Plan promote access to care for children who might face health disparity. **SDoH**

HEALTH CONCERNS AND LEADING CAUSES OF DEATH

CHILDREN

- Perinatal conditions and congenital anomalies
- Sudden unexplained infant death (SUID)
- Motor vehicle and other unintentional injuries
- Infant mortality associated with maternal health, socioeconomic status, and access to medical care

ADOLESCENTS

- Motor vehicle and other unintentional injuries
- Homicide
- Suicide

SCREENING AND PREVENTIVE SERVICES

CHILDREN

- Height and weight
- Vision and hearing
- Dental health
- At birth: hemoglobinopathy, phenylalanine level, T4, TSH
- Immunization status (Check the Centers for Disease Control and Prevention [CDC] website for current administration schedules.)
- Lead exposure
- Cholesterol and triglyceride levels
- Nutrition assessment
- Physical activity assessment

ADOLESCENTS

- Height and weight
- Vision and hearing
- Dental health
- Rubella serology and immunization history
- Substance use disorders, including tobacco
- Immunization status
- Mental health screenings
- Cholesterol and triglyceride levels
- Nutrition assessment
- Physical activity assessment

NATIONAL HEALTH GOALS Q_{EBP}

CHILDREN

Reductions in
- Dental caries
- Obesity
- Infant mortality
- Exposure to secondhand smoke

Increases in
- Newborn blood spot screenings and follow-up testing
- Access to a medical home **SDoH**
- Schools that require health education
- Childhood immunizations
- Use of child safety restraints
- Physical activity
- The number of infants who are breastfed

ADOLESCENTS

Reductions in
- Violent crimes
- Use of alcohol, marijuana, and illicit drugs
- Deaths related to motor vehicle crashes
- Mental health concerns

Increases in
- Schools with a breakfast program
- Participation in extracurricular activities
- Wellness checkups
- Physical activity

COMMUNITY EDUCATION

CHILDREN

- Anticipatory guidance
- Breastfeeding
- Sleeping positions
- Nutrition
- Physical activity
- Substance use disorders
- Dental hygiene and health
- Skin protection
- Injury prevention including car, fire, water safety; helmet use; poison control; CPR training

ADOLESCENTS

- Anticipatory guidance
- Substance use disorders
- Sexual behavior
- Nutrition, especially calcium intake for female clients
- Physical activity
- Skin protection
- Injury prevention including car, fire, and firearm safety

Adults

Adult health can be influenced by many factors. The genetic makeup of each sex can increase the risk for certain diseases. The environment is an influence, with societal and cultural expectations for gender influencing the risk of disease, and whether interventions for prevention and treatment of disease are valued. Most social determinants of health of the major health concerns for adults are related to chronic conditions, rather than infectious diseases. While screening recommendations are generalized for the aggregate, the nurse should also consider individual client factors when suggesting screenings.

Despite large expenditures on health, life expectancy for adults in the United States is lower than many other developed countries.

HEALTH CONCERNS AND LEADING CAUSES OF DEATH

- Heart disease
- Diabetes mellitus
- Mental health disorders
- Sexually transmitted infections
- Colorectal cancer (cancers of all types are a public health concern)
- Stroke
- Obesity

FEMALES

- Reproductive health
  - Childbearing
  - Menopause
  - Preconception counseling
- Malignant neoplasm (breast, cervix, ovaries)
- Osteoporosis

MALES

- Unintentional injuries
- Erectile dysfunction
- Malignant neoplasm (prostate, testes)

SCREENING AND PREVENTIVE SERVICES

- Height and weight
- Dental health
- Blood pressure
- Cholesterol (ages 45 to 65 years)
- Fecal occult blood test/sigmoidoscopy (45 years and older)
- Immunization status
- Diabetes mellitus
- HIV/STI
- Skin cancer
- Nutritional screening (obesity)
- Depression screening

FEMALES

- Pap test
- Mammogram and clinical breast exam
- Rubella serology and vaccination history (childbearing years)

MALES

- Digital rectal examination
- Prostate-specific antigen testing

NATIONAL HEALTH GOALS Q̲EBP

Reductions in
- Diseases involving bone, such as osteoporosis
- Death from cancer
- Sexual violence
- Incidence of HIV and AIDS
- Fatal and nonfatal injuries
- Unplanned pregnancies
- Excessive alcohol use and tobacco use

Increases in
- Use of both barrier and hormonal contraception
- Pregnant clients who receive early and adequate prenatal care
- Ability to identify warning indicators of a heart attack and stroke
- Abstinence from alcohol, nicotine, other substances among pregnant clients

COMMUNITY EDUCATION

- Nutrition
- STI prevention
- Substance use disorders
- HIV prevention
- Injury prevention including car, fire safety, violence
- Breast and testicular self-examination

Older adults

- The percentage of older adults compared to the general population continues to increase and is the fastest growing aggregate in the United States population.
- The proportion of older adults living alone has continued to increase. The community nurse should ensure clients living alone have access to the healthcare services and assistance needed. **SDoH**
- About one third of the medications prescribed in the United States are for older adult clients.
- Most older adults have at least one chronic health concern. Many have more than one, with some being particularly vulnerable due to age-related changes in physiologic functioning and the decreased ability to recover from illness and injury.
- The Administration on Aging, under the Older Americans Act, promotes health services for older adults through states, using local nonprofit agencies funded by the U.S. government.
- Healthy People has a topic area specific to older adult health. Health promotion targeting the aggregate of older adults affects individual health and the health of the general population.

NATIONAL HEALTH GOALS Q EBP

Reductions in

- The proportion of older adults who have moderate to severe functional limitations
- Hospitalizations due to heart failure
- Inappropriate medication use by older adults who have a disability
- Hospitalizations due to pressure injuries
- Emergency department visits due to falls

Increases in

- Use of clinical preventive services
- Use of the "Welcome to Medicare" benefit
- Information to the public regarding elder abuse, neglect, exploitation
- Physical activity among those who have reduced physical or cognitive function
- Access to diabetes self-management benefits
- Health care professionals who have geriatric certifications

COMMUNITY EDUCATION

- Community resources and programs
- Healthy meals and snacks, nutritional supplements
- Exercise
- Dental health
- Injury prevention
- Car and fire safety
- Fall prevention
- Abuse and mistreatment
- Medication safety

Families

The family as a client is basic to community-oriented nursing practice. Community health nurses have a significant role to play in promoting healthy families.

A family consists of individuals who identify themselves as family members and have an interdependent relationship that provides emotional, financial, and/or physical support. There are numerous structures and forms families can choose to take.

- Community health nurses must engage in community assessment, planning, development, and evaluation activities that are focused on family issues.
- Home visits provide community health nurses with the opportunity to observe the home environment and to identify barriers and supports to health-risk reduction.

APPROACHES

The nurse can take several different approaches to the nursing care of a family.

Family as a component of society

- Monitors how families interact with other institutions in a community (schools, medical facilities, financial institutions, congregations) **SDoH**
- Used to study and implement population-focused interventions (such as immunization campaigns for a disadvantaged population)

Family as a system

- Studies how interactions among family members affect the whole family function
- Used to promote family health by directing interventions toward the way family members interact with each other

Family as a client

- Examines the family unit functioning first, then individual needs next
- Used to see how the family health is impacted by each individual's reaction to a health event

Family as context

- Focuses on an individual first, and the family next
- Used to promote the health and recovery of an individual, using the family as a resource for service and support

CRISIS AND TRANSITIONS

Family crisis occurs when a family is not able to cope with an event. The family's resources are inadequate for the demands of the situation.

Transitions are times of risk for families.
• Transitions include birth or adoption of a child, death of a family member, child moving out of the home, marriage of a child, major illness, divorce, and loss of the main family income.
• These transitions require families to change behaviors, make new decisions, reallocate family roles, learn new skills, and learn to use new resources.

CHARACTERISTICS OF HEALTHY FAMILIES

• Members communicate well and listen to each other.
• There is affirmation and support for all members.
• Members teach respect for others.
• There is a sense of trust.
• Members play and share humor together.
• Members interact with one another.
• Members participate in leisure activities together.
• Members share a religious foundation.
• Privacy of individuals is respected.
• There is a shared sense of responsibility.
• There are traditions and rituals.
• Members seek help for their problems.

FAMILY HEALTH RISK APPRAISAL

BIOLOGICAL HEALTH RISK ASSESSMENT
• Genograms are used to gather basic information about the family, relationships within the family, and health and illness patterns. Genomics involves the study of genetic information and how it is influenced and expressed. Providers can use genomic information to identify specific individual risks and provide appropriate prevention.
• Repetitions of diseases with a genetic component (cancer, heart disease, diabetes mellitus) can be identified.
• Ecomaps are a visual diagram of the family unit in relation to other units (school, work, church, work, friends, extended family) used to understand the relationship among family members and the community.

ENVIRONMENTAL RISK: Ecomaps are used to identify family interactions with other groups and organizations. Information about the family's support network and social risk is gathered.

BEHAVIORAL RISK: Information is gathered about the family's health behavior, including health values, health habits, and health risk perceptions.

A Social Determinant of Health (SDOH) that can influence family health is economic stability, particularly assess to nutritious food. Some examples of health risks related to food insecurity for different age groups within a family are: **SDoH**
• Children: Anemia, poor cognitive ability, anxiety, asthma, and poor oral health.
• Adults: Depression, hypertension, hyperlipidemia, and sleep disorders.
• Senior adults: Poor overall physical health and depression

NATIONAL HEALTH GOALS Q EBP

Reductions in
• Barriers to access
• Allergens within the home
• Families that are unable to have a child or maintain a pregnancy
• Passive smoke exposure
• Household hunger
• Intimate partner violence

Increases in
• Positive parenting
• Health education provided by an agency (Head Start, school system, college, places of employment, health departments)
• Home testing for radon
• Health insurance coverage
• Individuals who have a usual primary care provider
• Family health literacy

Active Learning Scenario

A nurse is developing programs to promote the health of families in the local community. Use the *ATI Active Learning Template: Basic Concept* to complete this item.

RELATED CONTENT: Describe three characteristics of healthy families.

UNDERLYING PRINCIPLES
• Include two times families experience transition.
• Include two national health goals that apply to families.

NURSING INTERVENTIONS: Explain two strategies to improve the health of families.

Application Exercises

1. A public health nurse is planning an in-service on older adult health. Which of the following information should the nurse include?

   A. The percentage of older adults in the population is decreasing.

   B. The proportion of older adults who live alone is increasing.

   C. Older adults take one-half of all prescription medications.

   D. Older adults have a decreased recovery time following injury.

2. A home health nurse is planning care with a client and their family following a stroke. Match each approach to family nursing care with a strategy for using it to plan care.

   A. Family as a component of society

   B. Family as a system

   C. Family as a client

   D. Family as a context

   1. View the client as the focus of care with the family members viewed as a source of support for the client.

   2. Ask the family members how their family function overall has changed following the client's stroke.

   3. Ask individual family members how their life has changed following the client's stroke.

   4. Examine how the family unit interacts with other parts of society, such as with medical facilities or financial institutions.

3. A community health nurse is using tools to conduct a family assessment. Identify the following information gathered by the nurse by whether it is more likely to be included in a Genogram or an Ecomap.

   A. Family history of heart disease

   B. Family involvement in church activities

   C. Ages of everyone in the family

   D. Birth order of children

   E. Occupations of family members

   F. History of family violence

   G. Relationships with neighbors

   H. Schools the children in the family are attending

4. A nurse is planning interventions for populations of different age groups in the community. Sort the following educational topics by the population in which it is a major concern: School-Age Children, Adults, or Older Adults.

   A. Dental health

   B. Pneumococcal vaccine

   C. Preconception testing

   D. Accessing Medicare benefits

   E. Congenital anomalies

   F. Managing osteoporosis

   G. STI prevention

Active Learning Scenario Key

Using the ATI Active Learning Template: Basic Concept

RELATED CONTENT

- Members communicate well and listen to each other.
- There is affirmation and support for all members.
- Members teach respect for others.
- There is a sense of trust.
- Members play and share humor together.
- Members interact with one another.
- Members participate in leisure activities together.
- Members share a religious foundation.
- Privacy of individuals is respected.
- There is a shared sense of responsibility.
- There are traditions and rituals.
- Members seek help for their problems.

UNDERLYING PRINCIPLES

- Times of transition
  - Birth of a child
  - Adoption of a child
  - Death of a family member
  - Child moving from the home
  - Child getting married
  - Major illness of a family member
  - Divorce of a family member
  - Loss of the main source of family income
- National health goals
  - Reductions in
    - Barriers to access
    - Allergens within the home
    - Families that are unable to have a child or maintain a pregnancy
    - Passive smoke exposure
    - Household hunger
    - Intimate partner violence
  - Increases in
    - Positive parenting
    - Health education provided by an agency
    - Home testing for radon
    - Health insurance coverage
    - Individuals with a usual primary care provider

NURSING INTERVENTIONS

- Identify barriers and supports to health-risk reduction.
- Assess safety during home visits.
- Identify and coordinate needed community resource referrals.
- Perform biological health risk assessments.
- Assess for environmental and behavioral risks.

Ⓝ *NCLEX® Connection: Health Promotion and Maintenance, Health Promotion/Disease Prevention*

Application Exercises Key

1. A. The percentage of older adults in the population is increasing.
   B. **CORRECT:** The nurse should plan to teach the group that the number of older adults living alone continues to increase.
   C. Older adults take one-third of all prescription medications.
   D. Older adults have an increased recovery time following injury.

   Ⓝ *NCLEX® Connection: Health Promotion and Maintenance, Aging Process*

2. A, 4; B, 3; C, 2; D, 1

   When generating solutions using the family as a component of society approach, the nurse plans to examine how the family unit interacts with other parts of society to implement population-focused interventions. When using the family as a system approach, the nurse plans to ask each family member how their life has changed to direct interventions toward the way family members interact with each other. When using the family as a client approach, the nurse plans to ask each family member how their family function has changed to see how the family health is impacted by each individual's reaction to a health event. When using the family as context approach, the nurse views the client as the focus of care, with the family members viewed as a source of support for the client to promote the health and recovery of the individual.

   Ⓝ *NCLEX® Connection: Health Promotion and Maintenance, Health Screening; Psychosocial Integrity, Family Dynamics*

3. **GENOGRAM:** A, C, D, E, F; **ECOMAP:** B, G, H

   When recognizing cues while conducting a family assessment, a nurse may include a genogram or ecomap. A genogram is designed in a family tree format and includes family history and health-related information. Genograms contain information about family structure and timelines of events, such as domestic violence, substance abuse, and conflicts. An ecomap is designed in a large circle representing the family with smaller circles around it representing people, agencies, and organizations that are significant to the family. An ecomap includes the strengths of the relationships between the family and its supports, and well as the directional flow of energy with those relationships.

   Ⓝ *NCLEX® Connection: Health Promotion and Maintenance, Health Screening; Psychosocial Integrity, Family Dynamics*

4. **SCHOOL-AGE CHILDREN:** A, E; **ADULTS:** C, G; **OLDER ADULTS:** B, D, F

   The nurse should plan to generate solutions to address the needs of various age groups. Dental health, including fluoride, prevention of dental caries, and proper care of teeth and gums, is a major concern for school-age children. Preconceptual counseling is a major concern for adults during the reproductive years. Medicare provides health insurance coverage to older adults 65 years and older. Twenty-six percent of children have chronic health conditions, including Down syndrome, spina bifida, cerebral palsy, congenital heart disease, and attention-deficit/hyperactivity disorder (ADHD). About half of sexually transmitted every year are diagnosed in individuals ages 15 to 24 years. About half of women age 50 years and older will have a fracture related to osteoporosis, and 20% of people age 50 years and over who fracture a hip will die within one year. Pneumococcal vaccine is recommended for adults ages 65 years and older.

   Ⓝ *NCLEX® Connection: Health Promotion and Maintenance, Aging Process*

When reviewing the following chapter, keep in mind the relevant topics and tasks of the NCLEX outline, in particular:

Management of Care

CASE MANAGEMENT
Assess the client's need for materials and equipment.

Plan individualized care for client based on need.

LEGAL RIGHTS AND RESPONSIBILITIES: Identify legal issues affecting the client.

Psychosocial Integrity

ABUSE OR NEGLECT: Plan interventions for victims/suspected victims of abuse.

CHEMICAL AND OTHER DEPENDENCIES/SUBSTANCE USE DISORDER: Educate client on substance use diagnosis and treatment plan.

COPING MECHANISMS: Assess client's support systems and available resources.

STRESS MANAGEMENT: Assess stressors, including environmental, that affect client care.

Basic Care and Comfort

NONPHARMACOLOGICAL COMFORT INTERVENTIONS
Incorporate alternative/complementary therapies into client's plan of care.

Respect client's palliative care/symptom-management, non-curative treatments choices.

CHAPTER 7 *Care of Vulnerable Populations*

Community health nurses identify specific populations and implement measures to improve health through direct care or improving health care access, and by changing the physical environment, health care culture, and health policies.

Community health nurses care for many individuals who are members of specific populations and more prone to impaired health or negative outcomes associated with illness and disease. **SDoH**

FACTORS THAT CAN THREATEN HEALTH **SDoH**

- Low income
- Difficulty accessing health care, uninsured or underinsured
  - Uninsured or underinsured individuals access health services less often and have decreased management of chronic conditions.
- Poor self-esteem
- Young or advanced age
- Chronic stress
- Environmental factors
- Presence of communicable disease
- Racial and ethnic minority status
  - Individuals of ethnic or racial minorities often face social, environmental, and economic barriers. These barriers are linked to reduced access to care, decreased use of preventive care, and poorer health outcomes.
  - Disparities for minority groups differ across each population
  - Detailed information on the health status and concerns for minority populations in the United States is available through the Office of Minority Health website.
- Discrimination

SPECIFIC POPULATIONS

- There are populations that have multiple risk factors for negative health outcomes.
  - Identifying modifiable risk factors and targeting interventions can promote better health outcomes for the populations. This promotes population resilience.
- Some populations include individuals who are subject to issues such as the following.
  - Violence
  - Substance use disorders
  - Mental health issues/illnesses
  - Poverty and homelessness
  - Rural residency
  - Migrant employment
  - Veteran status
  - Disability

HEALTH DISPARITIES **SDoH**

Significant differences in health status and access to health services across varied groups.
- Health disparities can be linked to preferred sexual orientation, ethnicity, race, education, and income differences.
- Nurses should be aware of health disparities and intervene to reduce disparities when possible.
- The Healthy People initiative has a goal to eliminate disparities to achieve health equity.

NATIONAL HEALTH GOALS

Goals to address for individual populations include the following. **SDoH**
- Increasing the number of people who have a routine primary care provider
- Increasing the number of people who have health insurance
- Reducing the number of people who are unable to access, or have a delay in accessing, health care services and prescribed medications
- Reducing the number of people with disabilities who report physical barriers to accessing health and wellness programs in the community

NURSING ACTIONS

- Advocate for social justice and the elimination of health disparities.
- Create rapport and provide a safe environment.
- Be knowledgeable about population characteristics. When the client is an individual, investigate the individual's preferences that may differ from population trends.
- Facilitate care coordination among providers, facilities, and community resources.
- Advocate for the needs of the population, with focus on preventive services.
- Assist the client in obtaining as much control over personal health and health care as possible.
- Develop an interprofessional network to assist with improving the health of the population.

Violence

TYPES WITHIN COMMUNITIES

Homicide

- Homicide is often related to substance use.
- Most homicides are committed by someone known to the victim and occur during an argument.
- Violence often precedes homicide within families.
- Rates of homicide are increasing among adolescents more than in other age groups.

Assault

- Males are more likely than females to be assaulted.
- Youths are at a significantly increased risk.

Rape

- Rape is often unreported.
- Most incidences of rape are spousal (marital) or acquaintance (date) rape.
- Females are more likely than males to be raped. The risk of rape is increased in cities, between 8 p.m. and 2 a.m., on the weekends, and in the summer months.

Human Trafficking

- Human trafficking is a significant global public health issue, including in the United States.
- It affects all races, ages, and genders, but women and children under the age of 18 are at an increased risk.
- Understanding the issue and the available supports can be key to saving lives.

Suicide

- According to the CDC:
  - Rates of suicide are highest among individuals 35 to 64 years of age.
  - Females are more likely to attempt suicide; however, males are more likely to complete suicide.
  - Caucasians are more likely than other ethnic groups to commit suicide.
- Risk factors for suicide include depression or other mental health disorders, substance use, having access to a firearm, and partner violence or neglect issues.

Violence

PHYSICAL VIOLENCE occurs when pain or harm results.
- **Toward an infant or child,** as is the case with shaken baby syndrome (caused by violent shaking of young infants)
- **Toward a spouse or partner,** such as striking or strangling the partner
- **Toward an older adult** in the home (elder violence), such as pushing an older adult parent and causing her to fall Ⓖ
- **Toward a nonspouse or nonpartner**

SEXUAL VIOLENCE occurs when sexual contact takes place without consent.

EMOTIONAL VIOLENCE includes behavior that minimizes an individual's feelings of self-worth or humiliates, threatens, or intimidates a family member.

NEGLECT includes the failure to provide the following.
- **Physical care,** such as food, shelter, and hygiene
- **Emotional care** and/or stimulation necessary to achieve developmental milestones, such as speaking and interacting with a child
- **Education** for a child
- Needed **health or dental care**

INDIVIDUAL ASSESSMENT FOR VIOLENCE

INDIVIDUAL RISK FACTORS FOR VIOLENCE
- History of being abused or exposure to violence
- Low self-esteem
- Fear and distrust of others
- Poor self-control
- Inadequate social skills
- Minimal social support/isolation
- Immature motivation for marriage or childbearing
- Weak coping skills

RECOGNIZING POTENTIAL CHILD MALTREATMENT
- Unexplained injury
- Unusual fear of the nurse and others
- Injuries/wounds not mentioned in history
- Fractures, including older healed fractures
- Presence of injuries/wounds/fractures in various stages of healing
- Subdural hematomas
- Trauma to genitalia
- Malnourishment or dehydration
- General poor hygiene or inappropriate dress for weather conditions
- Parent considers child to be a "bad child, worthless, or burdensome."

ECONOMIC MALTREATMENT
- Failure to provide for the needs of a person in need when adequate funds are available
- Unpaid bills when another person is managing the finances
- Theft of or misuse of money or property

RECOGNIZING POTENTIAL OLDER ADULT ABUSE Ⓖ
- Unexplained or repeated physical injuries
- Physical neglect and unmet basic needs
- Rejection of assistance by caregiver
- Financial mismanagement
- Withdrawal and passivity
- Depression
- Mental anguish and fear

Community assessment

SOCIAL AND COMMUNITY VIOLENCE RISK FACTORS SDoH

- Work stress
- Unemployment
- Media exposure to violence
- Crowded living conditions
- Poverty
- Feelings of powerlessness
- Social isolation
- Lack of community resources (playgrounds, parks, theaters)

STRATEGIES TO REDUCE SOCIETAL VIOLENCE Qs

PRIMARY PREVENTION

- Teach alternative methods of conflict resolution, anger management, and coping strategies in community settings.
- Organize parenting classes to provide anticipatory guidance of expected age-appropriate behaviors, appropriate parental responses, and forms of discipline.
- Educate clients about community services that are available to provide protection from violence.
- Promote public understanding about the aging process and about safeguards to ensure a safe and secure environment for older adults in the community. Ⓖ
- Assist in removing or reducing factors that contribute to stress by referring caretakers of older adult clients to respite services, assisting unemployed parents in finding employment, or increasing social support networks for socially isolated families.
- Encourage older adults and their families to safeguard their funds and property by getting more information about a financial representative trust, durable power of attorney, a representative payee, and joint tenancy.
- Teach individuals that no one has a right to touch or hurt another person, and make sure they know how to report cases of abuse.
- Advocate for legislation designed to support adult independence, assist caregivers, and increase funding for programs that supply services to low-income, at-risk individuals.

SECONDARY PREVENTION

- Identify and screen those at risk for abuse and individuals who are potential abusers.
- Assess and evaluate any unexplained bruises or injuries of any individual.
- Screen all pregnant women for potential abuse. This might be the one time in some women's lives that they can access the health care system on a regular basis.
- Refer sexual assault or rape survivors to a local emergency department for assessment by a sexual assault abuse team. Caution the client not to bathe following the assault because it will destroy physical evidence.

- Assess and counsel anyone contemplating suicide or homicide and refer the individual to the appropriate services.
- Assess and help offenders address and deal with the stressors that can be causing or contributing to the abuse (mental illness, substance use).
- Alert all involved about available resources within the community.

TERTIARY PREVENTION

- Establish parameters for long-term follow-up and supervision.
- Make resources in the community available to survivors of violence (telephone numbers of crisis lines and shelters).
- If court systems are involved, work with parents while the child is out of the home (in foster care).
- Refer all involved to mental health professionals for long-term assistance.
- Provide grief counseling to families following the death of a family member to suicide or homicide.
- Develop support groups for caregivers and survivors of violence.
- Support and educate the offender, even though a report must be made.

CARING FOR CLIENTS WHO EXPERIENCE VIOLENCE Qpcc

- Build trust and confidence with a client.
- Focus on the client rather than the situation.
- Assess for immediate danger.
- Provide emergency care as needed.
- Work with the client to develop a plan for safety.
- Make needed referrals for community services and legal options.
- If abuse is suspected or has occurred, complete mandatory reporting, following state and agency guidelines.

Substance use disorders

- Substance use disorders involve the maladaptive use of substances resulting in threats to an individual's health or social and economic functioning.
- Substance use disorders have significant effects on family dynamics and often lead to codependency.
- Substance use disorders negatively affect family life, public safety, and the economy. They cause more disability, death, and illness than any other health condition.
- Recovery from substance use disorders occurs over years and usually involves relapses. A strong support system, including 12-step programs and self-help groups for family members, is important.
- Community health nurses are front-line health professionals who are able to assist those who have substance use disorders.

DEPENDENCE

Dependence is a pattern of pathological, compulsive use of substances and involves physiological and psychological dependence.

- Cardinal indicators of dependence include manifestations of tolerance and withdrawal.
- Denial is also a primary indication of dependence and can include the following.
  - Defensiveness
  - Lying about use
  - Minimizing use
  - Blaming or rationalizing use
  - Intellectualizing
  - "Going with the flow" (agreeing there is a problem, vowing to make a change, but the change doesn't occur)

HEALTH PROBLEMS

Alcohol, tobacco, and other substance use disorders can cause multiple health problems, including the following.

- Low birth weight
- Congenital abnormalities
- Accidents
- Homicides
- Suicides
- Chronic diseases
- Violence
- Disability

ALCOHOL USE

- Alcohol is the most commonly used substance in the U.S. It is socially acceptable, as well as easily accessible.
- Alcohol is a depressant. Alcohol dulls the senses to outside stimulation and sedates the inhibitory centers in the brain.
- People who frequently and consistently drink alcohol develop a tolerance, an increased requirement for alcohol to achieve the desired effect.

EFFECT OF ALCOHOL

- The direct effect of alcohol is determined by the blood alcohol level.
- The body processes alcohol dependent on several factors.
  - Size and weight of the drinker
  - Sex (affects metabolism)
  - Carbonation (increases absorption)
  - Time elapsed during alcohol consumption
  - Food in the stomach
  - The drinker's emotional state
  - Type of alcohol
- Excess alcohol that is not metabolized circulates in the blood and affects the central nervous system and the brain.

WITHDRAWAL

- Following prolonged use, manifestations of alcohol withdrawal appear within 4 to 12 hr.
- It is important to determine the time of the last drink the client ingested in order to accurately monitor for manifestations of withdrawal.

MANIFESTATIONS OF WITHDRAWAL

- Irritability
- Tremors
- Nausea
- Vomiting
- Headaches
- Diaphoresis
- Anxiety
- Sleep disturbances
- Tachycardia
- Elevated blood pressure

TOBACCO USE

- Smoking is the most important preventable cause of death in the U.S., according to the Centers for Disease Control and Prevention. Q EBP
- Nicotine is a stimulant that temporarily creates a feeling of alertness and energy. Repeated use to avoid the subsequent "down" that will follow this period of stimulation leads to a vicious cycle of use.
- Tolerance to nicotine develops quickly.
- Electronic cigarettes (E-cigarettes) have gained popularity in the United States among adolescents and contain liquid nicotine that is heated into a vapor and inhaled.
- Cigarette smoking results in deep inhalation of smoke, which poses the greatest health risk (cancer, cardiovascular disease, respiratory disease).
  - Cigars, pipes, and smokeless tobacco increase the risk of cancers of the lips, mouth, and throat.
  - Passive smoking (exposure to secondhand smoke) poses considerable health risks (respiratory disease, lung cancer) to nonsmokers.

OTHER SUBSTANCES

Marijuana has a low level of toxicity. Although it is legal in some states, it is considered the most commonly used illegal substance in the U.S. Users can develop tolerance and dependence with long-term use, but withdrawal manifestations are minimal.

Other stimulants include caffeine, amphetamines, methamphetamines, and cocaine.

Other depressants include barbiturates, benzodiazepines, chloral hydrate, and GHB.

Opiates include morphine, heroin, codeine, and fentanyl.

Hallucinogens (psychedelics) produce anxiety, paranoia, impaired judgment, and hallucinations. Some examples are lysergic acid diethylamide (LSD), phencyclidine (PCP), and MDMA (ecstasy).

Inhalants are volatile substances that are inhaled (huffed). Death can result from acute cardiac dysrhythmias or asphyxiation.

INDIVIDUAL ASSESSMENT QPcc

- Establish rapport with the client. Pose questions in a matter-of-fact tone. Be nonjudgmental. Communicate that the purpose of questioning is because of the effects that different practices can have on an individual's health. Use therapeutic communication.
- Seek information about specific substances used, methods of use, and the quantity (packs, ounces) and frequency of use.
- Elicit information about consequences experienced (blackouts, overdoses, injuries to self/others, legal or social difficulties).
- Determine whether the individual perceives a substance use problem.
- Discuss the individual's history of previous rehabilitation experiences.
- Gather family history of substance use and social exposure to other substance users.

PHYSICAL ASSESSMENT FINDINGS

VITAL SIGNS: Vary depending on the substance being used.

APPEARANCE: Individual can appear disheveled with an unsteady gait.

EYES: Pupils can appear dilated or pinpoint; eyes may be red, with poor eye contact.

SKIN: Can be diaphoretic, cool, and/or clammy. Needle track marks or spider angiomas may be visible.

NOSE: Can be runny, congested, red, and/or cauliflower-shaped.

TREMORS: Fine or coarse tremors can be present.

STRATEGIES TO REDUCE SUBSTANCE USE DISORDERS

PRIMARY PREVENTION
- Increase public awareness, particularly among young people, regarding the hazards and risks of dependence associated with substance use (public education campaigns, school education programs).
- Encourage development of life skills.
- Assist in the formation of parental action and awareness groups, such as Mothers Against Drunk Driving (MADD).

SECONDARY PREVENTION
- Identify at-risk individuals and assist them with reducing sources of stress, including possible referral to social services to eliminate financial difficulties or other sources of stress.
- Screen individuals for substance use disorders.

TERTIARY PREVENTION
- Assist the client with developing a plan to avoid high-risk situations and to enhance coping and lifestyle changes.
- Refer the client to community groups, such as Alcoholics Anonymous (AA) and Narcotics Anonymous (NA).
- Monitor pharmacological management (nicotine replacement therapy, methadone programs).
- Provide emotional support to recovering substance users and their families, including positive reinforcement.

Mental health

National Alliance for the Mentally Ill (NAMI) is an advocacy group that works to reduce stigma and provide services for clients who have mental health disorders and for their families.
- Individuals who have severe mental illness can experience stigma, marginalization, lack of social support, and inadequate treatment.
- Mental illness is complex and influenced by multiple individual and community factors; therefore it requires a variety of nursing strategies.

CHARACTERISTICS OF MENTAL HEALTH DISORDERS

- Occur across the lifespan
- High risk of substance use disorders
- High suicide risk
- Increased occurrence of chronic disease

SPECIFIC DISORDERS

- Affective disorders (bipolar disorder, major depressive disorder)
- Anxiety disorders (obsessive-compulsive, panic, phobias, posttraumatic stress)
- Schizophrenia
- Dementia
- Conduct disorders
- Personality disorders

FACTORS AFFECTING MENTAL HEALTH

- Individual coping abilities
- Stressful life events (exposure to violence, disasters)
- Social events (recent divorce, separation, unemployment, bereavement)
- Chronic health problems
- Stigma associated with seeking mental health services

STRATEGIES FOR IMPROVING MENTAL HEALTH

PRIMARY PREVENTION
- Provide education to populations regarding mental health issues.
- Teach stress-reduction techniques.
- Implement parenting classes.
- Organize bereavement support groups.
- Promote protective factors (coping abilities) and risk factor reduction.

SECONDARY PREVENTION
- Screen to detect mental health disorders.
- Work directly with at-risk individuals, families, and groups through formation of therapeutic relationships.
- Conduct crisis intervention.

TERTIARY PREVENTION

- Perform medication monitoring.
- Provide mental health interventions.
- Make referrals to various groups of professionals, including support groups and rehabilitation services. Qtc
- Maintain the client's level of function to prevent relapse or frequent rehospitalization.
- Identify behavioral, environmental, and biological triggers that can lead to relapse.
- Assist the client in planning a regular lifestyle and minimizing sources of stress.
- Educate the client and family regarding medication adverse effects and potential interactions.

Migrant employment

- Seasonal and migrant workers are often employed in farming. Employment occurs during the time period required for caring for and harvesting crops.
- Migrant workers make a temporary home during employment at a specific location and can be paying for their family to live in a different, permanent home at the same time.
- Agricultural workers are not covered under common labor laws (Fair Labor Standards Acts, Occupational Safety and Health Administration protections). Minors 12 years old and older are not covered under the Child Labor Act and can work alongside family members, even under hazardous conditions.
- The Migrant Health Act provides funding for migrant health centers across the U.S., which serve about one-fifth of the migrant worker population. The Department of Labor has regulations regarding standards for migrant and seasonal agricultural workers.
- Most migrant farmworkers do not speak English as a first language and can face barriers of discrimination or ineligibility for services. Undocumented workers might not seek services due to fear of deportation. **SDoH**
- The nurse should use cultural competence to design care for individuals and groups of seasonal and migrant farmworkers. **SDoH**

HEALTH PROBLEMS OF MIGRANT WORKERS

- Dental disease
- Tuberculosis
- Chronic conditions
- Stress, anxiety, and other mental health concerns
- Leukemia
- Iron deficiency anemia
- Stomach, uterine, and cervical cancers
- Lack of prenatal care
- Higher infant mortality rates
- STIs, including HIV/AIDS

Pesticide exposure

Pesticide exposure is a significant problem among farm workers. Qs

SUBJECTIVE FINDINGS: Headache, dizziness, dyspnea, nausea, abdominal cramps, poor concentration, eye irritation

OBJECTIVE FINDINGS: Confusion, irritability, muscle weakness and twitching, nasopharyngeal irritation, vomiting, rash, shortness of breath

COMPLICATIONS: Long-term exposure is linked to cancer, reproductive problems, Parkinson's disease, liver damage, and behavioral issues. Impaired fetal development can occur among pregnant women exposed to pesticides, even from secondary exposure (contaminated clothing from a family member).

ISSUES IN MIGRANT HEALTH

- Food insecurity
- Inconsistent income with yearly cycles of unemployment
- Poor and unsanitary working and housing conditions
- Exposure to environmental pesticides in agricultural settings
- Less access to dental, mental health, and pharmacy services
- Inability to afford care
- Reduced availability of services (distance, transportation, hours of service, lack of health record tracking)
- Language barriers and cultural aspects of health care
- Discrimination
- Immigration status (fear that seeking services will lead to deportation)
- Behavioral health issues (depression, anxiety, post-traumatic stress disorder [PTSD], stress).
- Harassment and sexual abuse

STRATEGIES FOR MIGRANT HEALTH CARE

Ensure that the informational material provided incorporates language or cultural specifications. Consider reading ability and health literacy of individuals.

PRIMARY PREVENTION

- Educate clients regarding measures to reduce exposure to pesticides (hand washing after working, washing food picked from fields before consumption, changing clothes after work).
- Teach clients about accident prevention measures.
- Provide prenatal care.
- Mobilize preventive services (dental, immunizations).

SECONDARY PREVENTION

- Create testing programs for tuberculosis and prenatal diagnostic testing.
- Implement screening programs.
  - Pesticide exposure
  - Skin cancer
  - Chronic preventable diseases
  - Communicable diseases
  - Anemia (children)
- Mobilize primary care and emergency services.

TERTIARY PREVENTION

- Treat for manifestations of pesticide exposure.
- Promote rehabilitation after work-related musculoskeletal injuries.
- Educate clients who have diabetes mellitus or anemia regarding appropriate nutrition.

Veterans

- The Department of Veterans Affairs (VA) estimates there are 21.8 million veterans in the U.S.
  - Approximately 2 million are women.
  - Approximately 9.9 million are over the age of 65. Ⓖ
- Veterans' Health Administration (within the U.S. Department of Veterans Affairs) is responsible for purchasing coverage and delivering health care to veterans and dependents.
  - Nation's largest integrated health care system
  - Inpatient and outpatient services
    - Hospitals
    - Outpatient clinics
    - Home health services
    - Hospice and palliative care services
    - Nursing homes
    - Residential rehabilitation treatment programs
    - Readjustment counseling centers

VETERAN HEALTH ISSUES

- Mental health (posttraumatic stress disorder, traumatic stress reactions, anger, depression)
- Substance use disorders
- Suicide
- Infectious diseases
- Exposures to herbicides, chemicals, radiation
- Traumatic brain injuries
- Spinal cord injuries
- Traumatic amputations
- Cold injury
- Military sexual trauma
- Hearing impairments
- Visual impairments

STRATEGIES FOR VETERAN HEALTH CARE

- Coordinate referrals to available veteran resources.
- Advocate for continued strengthening of the Veterans Health Administration health care system.
- Assist clients with transitioning from active duty to veteran status.
- Ensure continuity of care between acute and outpatient settings.
- Develop partnerships with local agencies to strengthen resources and achieve mutual goals. Qᴛᴄ

POSSIBLE STAKEHOLDERS FOR PARTNERSHIPS

- State and local veteran groups
- Offices of rural health
- Local aging services
- Community service organizations
- State and local health departments
- Faith-based organizations
- Public safety departments
- Various media outlets
- Employment services

Disability

- Disability indicates a factor in the body, senses, or mind that affects the way a person interacts in the daily environment. Exact definitions are determined by specific agencies and groups based on data collection needs.
- Individual or group living environments (unsanitary conditions, poor nutrition, stress), aging, chronic illness, injury, substance use, and genetics can cause physiological or psychological disability.
- Clients who have disabilities can use different terminology to describe their conditions, including the terms disabled, challenged, or compromised.
- About one-fifth of the U.S. population reports having a disability, some to the extent that it prevents the individual from living alone. Globally, 650 million people have some form of disability.
- The Americans with Disabilities Act was the initial legislation to promote rights for individuals who have disabilities.
- The Individuals with Disabilities Education Act (IDEA) also promoted the rights of children who have disabilities and their parents. IDEA ensures free public education and accommodations to prepare the child for independent living, assists with funding of the education, and evaluates the effectiveness of the education. Qᴘᴄᴄ

EFFECTS OF DISABILITY

- Cost of chronic management
- Decreased employment rates
- Decreased household income and increased poverty rates
- Decreased opportunity for physical activity (physical impairment)
- Isolation and possible self-image issues
- Possible altered roles of family members
- Increased risk for abuse
- Possible inability to live independently
- Presence of comorbidities

NURSING ACTIONS

The nurse provides care to individuals with disabilities and their families, as well as to groups within the community.

- Implement primary prevention measures to prevent disability (such as responsible alcohol use to prevent liver damage).
- Identify disability and chronic disease as early as possible.
- Connect clients with appropriate resources to promote maximum self-care ability.
- Connect families with respite care and counseling.

- Advocate for the rights of individuals, families, and groups dealing with disabilities.
- Ensure public buildings are accessible to individuals who have physical disabilities.
- Implement programs to improve quality of life.

Other at-risk populations

IMMIGRANTS

- Immigrants often have a waiting period to receive financial assistance for medical care.
- Unauthorized immigrants are only eligible for immunizations, school lunch, treatment for communicable disease, and emergency care.

NURSING ACTIONS

- Use cultural competence when planning care.
- Identify risk factors specific to the culture and race.

REFUGEES

- Refugees are those who have been forced to leave their place of origin due to disaster, war, or threatening environment.
- Refugees are eligible for Temporary Assistance for Needy Families, Medicaid, and Supplemental Security Income.

NURSING ACTIONS

- Assess mental health status and coping following crisis.
- Help individuals apply for assistance programs.

PREGNANT ADOLESCENTS

- Limited education and job opportunities
- Increased risk for poverty and homelessness
- Increased risk for school problems
- Increased incidence of violence
- Increased risk of malnutrition
- Increased risk for low birth weight or premature infants

NURSING ACTIONS

- Assist with early identification of pregnant adolescents, including early initiation of prenatal care.
- Provide pregnancy counseling, including alternative courses of action.
- Provide instruction and encouragement in the parenting role in home and peer group settings.
- Assist in applying for assistance programs (prenatal services; Women, Infants, and Children [WIC]).
- Promote education about self-care during pregnancy.

INCARCERATED POPULATIONS

- Increased rates of mental health disorders (The presence of major mental health disorders increases the risk for multiple incarcerations.)
- Increased incidence of rape and assault in the prison system
- Health care regulated through the Federal Bureau of Prisons (Department of Justice) to promote rights of inmates
- Increased rates of chronic disease compared with the general population

NURSING ACTIONS

- Implement health promotion and counseling during routine care.
- Assist with the design of programs to re-integrate individuals into society.
- Foster follow-up with community mental health centers.
- Provide transitional care to reduce the risk of future violent behavior.

LESBIAN, GAY, BISEXUAL, TRANSGENDER, QUEER, INTERSEX, AGENDER/ASEXUAL (LGBTQIA)

- Can face barriers to adequate health care
- State variations in rights for benefits and adoptions
- Can face social stigma and discrimination
- Health disparities, including poorer mental health, increased risk for disability, and increased risk for substance use disorder

NATIONAL HEALTH GOALS

- Increase survey and monitoring systems that include standardized questions to allow individuals to identify sexual orientation, gender, and pronouns.
- Reduce adolescent bullying.
- Increase health insurance coverage.
- Reduce the proportion of persons who experience major depressive episodes.
- Reduce adult tobacco and illicit drug use.
- Increase the number of individuals who have a routine health care provider.

NURSING ACTIONS

- Advocate increasing access to care.
- Support the development or maintenance of healthy families. ○PCC
- Provide opportunities and safe environments for clients to discuss care concerns.

Application Exercises

1. A supervisor of school nurses is preparing a presentation about child maltreatment and neglect. When discussing manifestations, why does the nurse include possible manifestations such as underweight and poor hygiene with neglect instead of physical abuse?

2. A community health nurse is developing an education program on substance use disorders for a group of adolescents. Which of the following information should the nurse include when discussing nicotine and smoking?

   A. Smoking is the fifth-most preventable cause of death in the United States.

   B. Nicotine is a central nervous system depressant.

   C. Withdrawal effects from smoking are minimal.

   D. Tolerance to nicotine develops quickly.

3. A public health nurse is implementing strategies to improve the care of clients who have mental health issues. Match each situation to the level of prevention the nurse is providing.

A. Screening a client whose partner recently died for suicide risk.	1. Primary
B. Teaching a client who has schizophrenia about medication interactions.	2. Secondary
C. Providing support programs for new parents.	3. Tertiary

4. A community health nurse is providing primary, secondary, and tertiary interventions for migrant workers. Identify each action as primary, secondary, or tertiary prevention.

   A. Partner with employers to provide sunscreen for workers.

   B. Provide fliers about recognizing pesticide toxicity.

   C. Provide tuberculin skin testing.

   D. Partner with physical therapy clinics to provide treatment for back injuries.

   E. Educate workers about measures to decrease risks for musculoskeletal injuries.

   F. Provide nutrition education for workers who have complications of diabetes.

5. A public health nurse is meeting with community leaders about interventions to assist specific populations. Which statement should the nurse make when discussing health disparities among these populations?

   A. Some populations have multiple risk factors that impact their health outcomes.

   B. Some populations are more affected by nonmodifiable genetic factors than by social determinants of health.

   C. Some populations demonstrate chronic overuse of the health care system.

   D. Some populations have negative cultural beliefs about the health care system.

Active Learning Scenario

A nurse is reviewing data that will assist with the development of a program to improve health outcomes of specific populations. Use the *ATI Active Learning Template: Basic Concept* to complete this item.

RELATED CONTENT: List at least two national health goals that address specific populations.

UNDERLYING PRINCIPLES: List at least three issues that affect specific populations.

NURSING INTERVENTIONS: Include at least two strategies to improve access to health care for specific populations.

Active Learning Scenario Key

Using the ATI Active Learning Template: Basic Concept

RELATED CONTENT
- Increase the number of people who have a routine primary care provider.
- Increase the number of people who have health insurance.
- Reduce the number of people who are unable to access, or have a delay in accessing, health care services and prescribed medications.
- Reduce the number of people who have disabilities who report physical barriers to accessing health and wellness programs in the community.

UNDERLYING PRINCIPLES
- Violence
- Substance use disorders
- Homelessness
- Mental health issues
- Poverty
- Chronic stress
- Poor self-esteem
- Access to health care services

NURSING INTERVENTIONS
- Coordinate services at a central location.
- Develop programs that go to the population to deliver health care (home visits, health services bus, on-site clinics).
- Create partnerships to provide free or reduced health care services.
- Advocate for increased availability of health insurance for the uninsured and underinsured.
- Evaluate current health care systems and make recommendations that will strengthen access.
- Collaborate with community leaders to improve/increase the availability of public transportation.
- Ensure the availability of translators with medical training.

(N) *NCLEX® Connection: Management of Care, Advocacy*

Application Exercises Key

1. When generating solutions, the nurse should recognize that neglect occurs when a child's basic needs, such as nutrition and hygiene needs, are not met. Physical neglect often occurs in situations associated with poverty and includes failure to provide medical care, shelter, adequate clothing, hygiene, and food.

   (N) *NCLEX® Connection: Psychosocial Integrity, Abuse or Neglect*

2. A. Smoking is the leading preventable cause of death in the U.S.
   B. Nicotine is a central nervous system stimulant.
   C. Withdrawal effects from smoking are substantial and increase physical dependence.
   D. **CORRECT:** When generating solutions, the nurse recognizes that the body quickly develops tolerance to nicotine to protect itself from the toxic effects of nicotine.

   (N) *NCLEX® Connection: Health Promotion and Maintenance, High-Risk Behaviors*

3. A, 2; B, 3; C, 1

   When taking actions, the nurse implements primary prevention interventions when providing support programs, because primary prevention includes parenting classes, stress reduction, and promoting coping abilities. The nurse implements secondary prevention interventions when screening a client for suicide risk, because secondary prevention includes screening to detect mental health disorders. The nurse implements tertiary prevention interventions when teaching a client about medication interactions, because tertiary prevention includes education about medications.

   (N) *NCLEX® Connection: Psychosocial Integrity, Cultural Awareness/Cultural Influence on Health*

4. **PRIMARY:** A, E; **SECONDARY:** B, C; **TERTIARY:** D, F

   When taking actions, the nurse intervenes at the primary level of prevention by providing sunscreen and educating workers about injury prevention, because those actions prevent the development of illness and injury. The nurse intervenes at the secondary level of prevention by providing fliers about recognizing pesticide toxicity and providing tuberculin skin testing, because those actions are forms of screening for manifestations of illness or injury. The nurse intervenes at the tertiary level of prevention by providing treatments for back injuries and providing nutrition education for workers who have complications of diabetes, because those actions prevent existing illnesses or injuries from worsening.

   (N) *NCLEX® Connection: Psychosocial Integrity, Cultural Awareness/Cultural Influence on Health*

5. A. **CORRECT:** When taking actions, the nurse should discuss how specific populations have multiple risk factors for negative health outcomes that include gender, race, ethnicity, income differences, and education.

   (N) *NCLEX® Connection: Psychosocial Integrity, Cultural Awareness/Cultural Influence on Health*

When reviewing the following chapter, keep in mind the relevant topics and tasks of the NCLEX outline, in particular:

Management of Care

ESTABLISHING PRIORITIES: Prioritize the delivery of client care.

LEGAL RIGHTS AND RESPONSIBILITIES: Report client conditions as required by law.

Safety and Infection Control

EMERGENCY RESPONSE PLAN
Use clinical decision–making/critical thinking for emergency response plan.

Identify nursing roles in disaster planning.

Participate in emergency response plans.

Participate in disaster–planning activities/drills.

HANDLING HAZARDOUS AND INFECTIOUS MATERIALS: Follow procedures for handling biohazardous and hazardous materials.

STANDARD PRECAUTIONS/TRANSMISSION-BASED PRECAUTIONS/SURGICAL ASEPSIS: Understand communicable diseases and the modes of organism transmission.

Psychosocial Integrity

COPING MECHANISMS: Assess client's ability to cope with life changes, and provide support.

Physiological Adaptation

ALTERATIONS IN BODY SYSTEMS: Provide care to a client with an infectious disease.

ILLNESS MANAGEMENT: Apply knowledge of client pathophysiology to illness management.

CHAPTER 8 *Emergency Preparedness*

Large-scale events have highlighted the need for health care professionals to have knowledge of disaster management and bioterrorism.

Nurses have unique skills required to plan for and respond to natural and man-made disasters.

By understanding principles of emergency preparedness, the nurse can play a role in preventing large-scale events or minimizing the negative effects. The nurse collaborates with other agencies and promotes recovery.

Disasters

A disaster is an event that causes human suffering and demands more resources than are available in the community. A disaster can be naturally occurring, man-made, or a combination of both, such as a natural disaster causing technological failures. Disaster preparedness includes planning for all types of hazards and establishing protocols for managing the surge of clients in the health care system.

DISASTER MANAGEMENT CYCLE

DISASTER PREVENTION (MITIGATION)

- This includes activities to prevent natural and man-made disasters, such as increasing surveillance, improving inspections and airport security, and strengthening public health processes such as immunizations, isolation, and quarantine.
- Activities such as strengthening levees/barriers to prevent flooding and teaching methods of preventing communicable disease transmission are also components.
- The community's threats, vulnerabilities, and capabilities are determined, as are the demographics of community members.
- This level also includes identification and assessment of populations at risk. Ⓖ
  - Populations at risk are those that have fewer resources or less of an ability to withstand and survive a disaster without physical harm. **SDoH**
  - These populations tend to be physically isolated, disabled, or unable to access disaster services. Strategic emergency planning is necessary to prevent the loss of lives in susceptible populations.

8.1 Disaster management cycle

mitigation — preparedness — response — recovery — emergency management

DISASTER PREPAREDNESS Qₛ

- Disaster preparedness occurs at the national, state, and local levels. Personal and family preparedness are crucial components of disaster preparedness, as is professional preparedness for individuals employed in civil service and health care.
- Disaster preparations should stem from threats and vulnerabilities identified in the prevention level and should coordinate community efforts as well as outline specific roles of local agencies.
- This level of management includes preparedness for natural or man-made disasters.
- Individual and family disaster preparedness include creating an action plan and determining alternative methods of communication, highlighting possible evacuation routes, identifying local and distant meeting places, and creating a disaster kit.
- Setting up a communication protocol is an important part of community disaster planning. The communication plan should provide for access to emergency agencies, such as the American Red Cross and state and federal government agencies. Qᴛᴄ
- Disaster drills replicate possible scenarios in the local area and enhance preparedness of community members, government agencies, health care facilities, and businesses.

DISASTER RESPONSE

- The National Incident Management System (NIMS) provides a structure for managing any type of disaster, incorporating various public and private agencies. The goal is to have effective communication and a clear chain of command to manage disasters.
- Different agencies, governmental and nongovernmental, are responsible for different levels of disaster response. Some of the agencies with a role in disaster response include the Federal Emergency Management Agency (FEMA), the CDC, U.S. Department of Homeland Security (DHS), American Red Cross (ARC), Office of Emergency Management (OEM), and the public health system.
- Disaster management response includes an initial assessment of the span of the disaster.

- How many people are affected?
  - How many are injured or dead?
  - How much fresh water and food is available?
  - What are the areas of risk or sanitation problems?
- Disasters are classified according to type, level, and scope.
- If a federal emergency is declared, the National Response Framework (NRF) is activated and provides direction for an organized, effective national response.

DISASTER RECOVERY

- Recovery begins when danger no longer exists and needed representatives and agencies are available to assist with rebuilding.
- Recovery lasts until the economic and civil life of the community are restored, which can be days, weeks, or even years. At an individual level, it is the time it takes an individual to become functional within a community after a disaster.
- Communicable disease and sanitation controls are important aspects of disaster recovery.
- Post-traumatic stress disorder (PTSD) and delayed stress reactions (DSR) are common during the aftermath of disasters and can affect both caregivers and victims.

PHASES OF EMOTIONAL REACTION DURING A DISASTER

- **Heroic:** Intense excitement and concern for survival. Often a rush of assistance from outside the area is present.
- **Honeymoon:** Affected individuals begin to bond and relive their experiences.
- **Disillusionment:** Responders can experience depression and exhaustion. Phase contains unexpected delays in receiving aid.
- **Reconstruction:** Involves adjusting to a new reality and continued rebuilding of the area. Counseling is sometimes needed. Those affected begin looking ahead.

ROLES OF COMMUNITY HEALTH NURSES

RISK ASSESSMENT

Ask the following questions. Qs
- What are the populations at risk within the community?
- Have there been previous disasters, natural or man-made?
- What size of an area or population is likely to be affected in a worst-case scenario?
- What is the community disaster plan?
- What kind of warning system is in place?
- What types of disaster response teams (volunteers, nurses, health care providers, emergency medical technicians, firemen) are in place?
- What kinds of resource facilities (hospitals, shelters, churches, food-storage facilities) are available in the event of a disaster?
- What type of evacuation measures (boat, motor vehicle, train) will be needed?
- What type of environmental dangers (chemical plants, sewage displacement) can be involved?

DISASTER PLANNING

- Develop a disaster response plan based on the most probable disaster threats.
- Identify the community disaster warning system and communication center and learn how to access it.
- Identify the community's first responders' disaster plan.
- Make a list of agencies that are available for the varying levels of disaster management at the local, state, and national levels.
- Define the nursing roles in first-, second-, and third-level triage.
- Identify the specific roles of personnel involved in disaster response and the chain of command.
- Locate all equipment and supplies needed for disaster management, including hazmat suits, infectious control items, medical supplies, food, and potable (drinkable) water. Detail a plan to replenish these regularly.
- Check equipment (including evacuation vehicles) regularly to ensure proper operation.
- Evaluate the efficiency, response time, and safety of disaster drills, mass casualty drills, and disaster plans.
- Assist community members with personal preparedness by having a plan for evacuation and making a disaster kit. Kits should include at least 3 days' supply of food, water, medication, clothing, and hygiene items per person, copies of personal documents, and first aid supplies. The CDC and American Red Cross have lists of essential items for a disaster kit.
- Talk with medical facilities and governing agencies about crisis standards of care to determine how care standards might be altered to manage a large surge of clients.

DISASTER RESPONSE

- Activate the disaster management plan.
- Perform triage, direct those affected, and coordinate evacuation, quarantine, and opening of shelters.
- Triage involves identifying those who have serious versus minor injuries, prioritizing care of victims, and transferring those requiring immediate attention to medical facilities.
- Collaborate with response partners to develop plans for triage algorithms.
- Identify and place public health nurses and other support personnel to provide care according to the developed algorithms.

DISASTER RECOVERY

- Make home visits and reassess the health care needs of the affected population.
- Provide and coordinate care in shelters.
- Provide stress counseling and assessing for PTSD or delayed stress reactions and making referrals for psychological treatment.
- Monitor the physical and psychosocial environment.

EVALUATION OF DISASTER RESPONSE ⊙QI

- Evaluate the area, effect, and level of the disaster.
- Create ongoing assessment and surveillance reports.
- Evaluate the efficiency of the disaster response teams.
- Estimate the length of time for recovery of community services, such as electricity and running potable water.

Bioterrorism

AGENTS OF BIOTERRORISM

CATEGORY A BIOLOGICAL AGENTS
- The highest priority agents, posing a risk to national security because they are easily transmitted and have high mortality rates.
- Examples include smallpox, botulism, anthrax, tularemia, viral hemorrhagic fevers (Ebola), and plague.

CATEGORY B BIOLOGICAL AGENTS
- The second-highest priority because they are moderately easy to disseminate and have high morbidity rates and low mortality rates.
- Examples include typhus fever, ricin toxin, diarrheagenic E. coli, and West Nile virus.

CATEGORY C BIOLOGICAL AGENTS
- The third-highest priority, comprising emerging pathogens that can be engineered for mass dissemination because they are easy to produce, and/or have a potential for high morbidity and mortality rates.
- Examples include hantavirus, influenza virus, tuberculosis, and rabies virus.

BIOTERRORISM INCIDENTS

Inhalational anthrax

MANIFESTATIONS
- Headache
- Fever and chills
- Muscle aches
- Chest discomfort
- Severe dyspnea
- Shock

PREVENTION
- Anthrax vaccine can be used for those at high-risk for exposure to anthrax.
- Ciprofloxacin and doxycycline are recommended by the CDC for prevention of anthrax following exposure.

TREATMENT
Antitoxin and IV antibiotics are administered with two or more antimicrobial agents.

Botulism

MANIFESTATIONS
- Double or blurred vision
- Slurred speech
- Difficulty swallowing
- Progressive muscle weakness
- Difficulty breathing

PREVENTION: No approved vaccine

TREATMENT
- Airway management with possible mechanical ventilation
- Administration of antitoxin

ELIMINATION OF TOXIN: Induction of vomiting, enemas, surgical excision of wound tissue

SUPPORTIVE CARE: Nutrition, fluids, prevent complications

Smallpox

MANIFESTATIONS
- Findings include high fever, fatigue, and head and body aches.
- Rash begins on face and tongue; quickly spreads to the trunk, arms, and legs, then hands and feet; then turns to pus-filled lesions.
- Onset is a sudden fever with severe aches and possible vomiting.
- Rash appears 2 to 4 days after fever (more on face and limbs than trunk).
- Lesions are all in the same stage of development, deep vesicles, and do not collapse when punctured.

PREVENTION
- Administer vaccine for those at high risk (provides 10 years of immunity). Vaccine can be given within 3 days of exposure.
- Follow contact and airborne precautions.
- Teach health care professionals to distinguish smallpox lesions from chickenpox lesions.
  - The onset of chickenpox is rapid with mild fever and aches.
  - Chickenpox rash is present from manifestation onset and is primarily on the trunk.
  - Chickenpox lesions appear in various stages of development and are superficial. Vesicles collapse when punctured.

TREATMENT
Two antiviral medications approved by the FDA based on efficacy in animals for treatment of smallpox.
- Tecovirimat: approved in 2018. Available in CDC Strategic National Stockpile (SNS) in the event of an outbreak
- Brincidofovir: approved in 2021

SUPPORTIVE CARE: Hydration, pain medication, antipyretics, antibiotics for secondary infections

Ebola

TRANSMISSION: Contaminated body fluids of individuals exhibiting manifestation of infection

MANIFESTATIONS
- Fever
- Severe headache
- Joint and muscle aches
- Fatigue and weakness
- Hemorrhage
- Vomiting and diarrhea
- Shock
- Sore throat
- Loss of appetite

PREVENTION
- First FDA approved Ebola vaccine approved in 2019Don impermeable gown or coverall; disposable gloves (two pairs), boot covers, and apron; and N95 mask. Recommend a second caregiver supervise doffing. Maintain droplet and contact isolation precautions.
- Prevent contact with semen of a previously infected client until testing shows that the virus is gone from the semen.
- Avoid contact with items that may have come in contact with an infected person's body fluids (clothes, bedding, needles, medical equipment).

TREATMENT
- Supportive care IV fluids, dialysis, airway management, psychological counseling.
- Minimize invasive procedures.
- Two treatments were approved by the FDA in 2020 for treatment of the Zaire ebolavirus
  - Mixture of three antibodies: atoltivimab, maftivimab, and odesivimab-ebgn
  - Single antibody: ansuvimab-zykl

Plague

MANIFESTATIONS
These forms can occur separately or in combination.
- **Pneumonic plague:** fever, headache, weakness, pneumonia with shortness of breath, chest pain, cough, and bloody or watery sputum
- **Bubonic plague:** swollen, tender lymph nodes, fever, headache, chills, and weakness
- **Septicemic plague:** fever, chills, weakness, prostration, abdominal pain, shock, disseminated intravascular coagulation (DIC), gangrene of nose and digits

PREVENTION
- Vaccine no longer available in the U.S.
- Contact precautions until decontaminated if exposed to bubonic plague or suspected gross contamination
- Droplet precautions until 72 hr after antibiotics if exposed to pneumonic plague

TREATMENT: Gentamicin and fluoroquinolones

Tularemia

MANIFESTATIONS
- Sudden fever, chills, headache, diarrhea, muscle aches, joint pain, dry cough, progressive weakness
- If airborne, life-threatening pneumonia and systemic infection

PREVENTION: Vaccine under review by the Food and Drug Administration, but not currently available

TREATMENT
- Streptomycin or gentamicin is the antibiotic of choice.
- In mass causality, use doxycycline or ciprofloxacin.

DELIVERY MECHANISMS FOR BIOLOGICAL AGENTS

- Direct contact (subcutaneous anthrax)
- Simple dispersal device (airborne, nuclear)
- Water and food contamination
- Droplet or blood contact

ROLES OF COMMUNITY HEALTH NURSES

- Participate in planning and preparation for immediate response to a bioterrorism event.
- Identify potential biological agents for bioterrorism.
- Survey for and report bioterrorism activity (usually to the local health department).
- Promptly participate in measures to contain and control the spread of infections resulting from bioterrorism activity.

ASSESSMENT OF THREAT Qs

- Is the population at risk for sudden high disease rates?
- Is the vector that normally carries a specific disease available in the geographical area affected?
- Is there a potential delivery system within the community?

RECOGNITION OF A BIOTERRORISM EVENT

- Is there a rapidly increasing disease incidence in a normally healthy population?
- Is a disease occurring that is unusual for the area?
- Is an endemic occurring at an unusual time? For example, is there an outbreak of influenza in the summer?
- Are there large numbers of people dying rapidly with similar presenting manifestations?
- Are there any individuals presenting with unusual manifestations?
- Are there unusual numbers of dead or dying animals, unusual liquids/vapors/odors?

LEVELS OF PREVENTION

PRIMARY PREVENTION: Bioterrorism planning
- Prepare with bioterrorism drills, vaccines, and ensuring availability of antibiotics for exposure prophylaxis.
- Design a bioterrorism response plan using the most probable biological agent in the local area.
- Identify the chain of command for reporting bioterrorism attacks.
- Define the nursing roles in the event of a bioterrorism attack.
- Set up protocols for different levels of infection control and containment.

SECONDARY PREVENTION: Early recognition
- Activate the bioterrorism response plan in response to a bioterrorism event.
- Immediately implement infection control and containment measures, including decontamination, environmental disinfection, protective equipment, community education/notification, and quarantines.
- Screen the population for exposure, assessing rates of infection and administering vaccines as available.
- Assist with and educate the population regarding identification of manifestations and management (immunoglobulin, antiviral, antitoxins, and antibiotic therapy, depending on the agent).
- Monitor mortality and morbidity.

TERTIARY PREVENTION: Rehabilitation of survivors
- Monitor medication regimens and referrals.
- Evaluate effectiveness and timeliness of the bioterrorism plan.

Active Learning Scenario

A community health nurse is responding to a man-made disaster in the local community. Use the *ATI Active Learning Template: Basic Concept* to complete this item.

UNDERLYING PRINCIPLES
- Include three agencies involved in disaster response.
- List two questions to ask to determine the disaster's scope.

NURSING INTERVENTIONS: Explain four disaster response nursing roles.

Application Exercises

1. A public health nurse cares for a community through all phases of the disaster management cycle. Match each action to the phase in which the nurse will implement it.

   A. Prioritize care of individuals.
   B. Outline specific roles of community agencies.
   C. Provide stress counseling.
   D. Identify community vulnerabilities.

   1. Disaster preparedness
   2. Disaster prevention
   3. Disaster response
   4. Disaster recovery

2. A community health nurse is preparing a presentation for community leaders about the phases of emotional reaction during a disaster. Place the phases in the order the nurse plans to discuss them from first to final.

   A. Disillusionment
   B. Honeymoon
   C. Reconstruction
   D. Heroic

3. A public health nurse is interviewing a group of people several weeks after a community tornado. Identify the following statements made by the group members as honeymoon, disillusionment, or reconstruction phases.

   A. "I am tired and don't think I'll ever be able to fix everything."
   B. "I am so grateful we survived. I keep telling everyone what happened."
   C. "Things will never be the same, but we will find a way to go on."
   D. "Our neighborhood is working together to make good changes."
   E. "My old hobbies don't seem interesting anymore since the tornado."
   F. "I just don't understand why it's taking so long to make the repairs."

4. A community health nurse is educating a group of community leaders about agents of bioterrorism. Identify each biological agent as category A, B, or C.

   A. Hantavirus
   B. Typhus
   C. Plague
   D. Tularemia
   E. Botulism
   F. E. coli

5. A public health nurse is reviewing reports about potential bioterrorism incidents. Which of the following findings does nurse recognize as an indication of potential bioterrorism?

   A. Nationwide incidence of pneumonia is higher than the prior year.
   B. A large number of otherwise healthy adults in a county are dying from sepsis.
   C. A city health department reports cases of influenza in October.
   D. Most clients in a local population who have pneumonia have an elevated white blood cell count.

Active Learning Scenario Key

Using the ATI Active Learning Template: Basic Concept

UNDERLYING PRINCIPLES

Involved agencies
- FEMA
- CDC
- U.S. Department of Homeland Security
- American Red Cross
- Office of Emergency Management

Disaster scope
- How many people are affected?
- How many are injured or dead?
- How much potable water and food is available?
- What are the areas of risk or sanitation problems?

NURSING INTERVENTIONS
- Activate the disaster management plan.
- Perform triage and direct disaster victims.
- Collect data using surveillance to identify the scope of the problem.
- Communicate with other responders following National Incident Management System standards.
- Coordinate evacuation or quarantines.
- Open shelters.
- Promote community recovery using physical, financial, and psychosocial resources.

Ⓝ *NCLEX® Connection: Safety and Infection Control, Emergency Response Plan*

Application Exercises Key

1. A, 3; B, 1; C, 4; D, 2

   When taking actions, the nurse will outline specific roles of community agencies during the disaster preparedness phase, identify community vulnerabilities during the disaster prevention phase, prioritize care of individuals during the disaster response phase, and provide stress counseling during the disaster recovery phase.

   Ⓝ *NCLEX® Connection: Safety and Infection Control, Emergency Response Plan*

2. D, B, A, C. **CORRECT:** When generating solutions, the nurse plans to first discuss the heroic phase, in which affected community members are mostly concerned for safety and survival. The nurse plans to next discuss the honeymoon phase, in which affected community members share and relive their experiences during the disaster event. The next phase the nurse plans to discuss is disillusionment, in which affected individuals experience exhaustion and disappointment. The final phase the nurse plans to discuss is reconstruction, in which community members are rebuilding, resuming normal activities, and looking ahead.

   Ⓝ *NCLEX® Connection: Safety and Infection Control, Emergency Response Plan*

3. **HONEYMOON:** B; **DISILLUSIONMENT:** A, E, F; **RECONSTRUCTION:** C, D

   When analyzing cues, the nurse identifies statements that include thankfulness and sharing experiences as part of the honeymoon phase after a disaster incident. The nurse identifies expressions of disappointment, frustration, fatigue, and gloom as part of the disillusionment phase after a disaster incident. The nurse identifies statements that include rebuilding and establishing a new normal as part of the reconstruction phase.

   Ⓝ *NCLEX® Connection: Safety and Infection Control, Emergency Response Plan*

4. **CATEGORY A:** C, D, E; **CATEGORY B:** B, F; **CATEGORY C:** A

   When taking actions, the nurse should discuss plague, tularemia, and botulism as examples of Category A agents of bioterrorism. The nurse should discuss typhus and E. coli as examples of Category B agents of bioterrorism. The nurse should discuss hantavirus as an example of a Category C agent of bioterrorism.

   Ⓝ *NCLEX® Connection: Safety and Infection Control, Emergency Response Plan*

5. B. **CORRECT:** When analyzing data, the nurse should recognize that clustering of disease manifestations in an area could result from a bioterrorism attack.

   Ⓝ *NCLEX® Connection: Safety and Infection Control, Emergency Response Plan*

When reviewing the following chapter, keep in mind the relevant topics and tasks of the NCLEX outline, in particular:

Management of Care

CASE MANAGEMENT: Provide client with information on discharge procedures to home, or community setting.

CLIENT RIGHTS: Advocate for client rights and needs.

ETHICAL PRACTICE: Practice in a manner consistent with a code of ethics for nurses.

REFERRALS: Identify community resources for the client.

CONCEPTS OF MANAGEMENT: Act as liaison between client and others.

PERFORMANCE IMPROVEMENT (QUALITY IMPROVEMENT): Define performance improvement/quality assurance activities.

Health Promotion and Maintenance

SELF CARE
Assess client ability to manage care in the home environment and plan care accordingly.

Consider client self care needs before developing or revising care plan.

CHAPTER 9 Continuity of Care

Community health nurses play a large role in maintaining continuity of care for clients as they transition from acute to outpatient settings. The increase in prevalence of chronic disease means that an increased number of clients will transition into and out of acute settings, and require support from community agencies to address medical, financial, and personal needs. Community health nurses use technology to maintain continuity of care.

Community partnerships are essential to improving and maintaining healthy communities. Community health nurses should facilitate the development of partnerships within the community. These partnerships are important in the attainment of collaborative health outcomes.

EXAMPLES OF PARTNERING ENTITIES

- Individuals
- Families
- Community agencies
- Civic organizations
- Citizen groups
- Educational settings
- Political offices
- Employment bureaus
- Faith based organizations

CHARACTERISTICS OF SUCCESSFUL PARTNERSHIPS

- Shared power
- Shared goals
- Integrity
- Flexibility
- Negotiation

Groups partnering to elicit needed change in the community are more powerful than a nurse working independently with an individual

Referrals, discharge planning, and case management

- A continuum of care assists in coordinating and providing individualized health care services without disruption. The nurse can follow the client from one level of care to the next to ease the client's transition.
- Community health nurses facilitate continuity of care through case management services. These services include focused supervision for individualized care, follow-up, and referrals to appropriate resources. Qpcc
- The establishment of an ongoing relationship between an individual and a health care provider leads to improved health outcomes.

CONSULTATIONS

A consultant is someone who has specialized knowledge and provides expert advice, services, or information.

NURSING ACTIONS

- Initiate necessary consults, or notify the provider of the client's needs so the provider can initiate a consult.
- Seek expertise from health care professionals representing a variety of disciplines.
- Request expert opinions of key community members, agency leaders, and other professionals.
- Seek expertise of other nurses, such as specialty nurses (psychiatric nurse, school nurse, gerontological nurse, diabetes management nurse), or advanced practice nurses (psychiatric mental health nurse practitioner, gerontological nurse practitioner).
- Incorporate recommendations from a consultant into the client's plan of care or program planning for the community.

9.1 Case management continuum of health care

- Coordinate recommendations from multiple consultants (providers, advanced practice nurses, pharmacists, dietitians, therapists, holistic providers) to ensure client safety. Qs
- Serve as an expert witness in legal proceedings.
- Serve as a consultant regarding the health care needs of individuals, families, and groups within the community served.

REFERRALS

- Referrals for individuals in acute care settings typically are based on the medical diagnosis or other relevant clinical information. Resources assist in restoring, maintaining, or promoting health.
- The nurse assists in linking the client with community resources and must have knowledge of individuals and organizations that can serve as resources. The nurse should also use knowledge of types of assistance the client will accept based on client's personal beliefs and values. Qpcc
- The nurse educates clients about community resources and self-care measures.

HEALTH CARE SERVICES

- Providers
- Acute-care settings
- Primary care sites
- Health departments
- Transitional and long-term care facilities
- Home care services
- Rehabilitation services
- Physical therapy services
- Occupational therapy services
- Pharmacies

SPECIALTY SERVICE AGENCIES

- Support Services
- Psychological services
- Faith community centers
- Support groups
- Life care planners
- Medical equipment providers
- Health insurance companies
- Meal delivery services
- Transportation services

BARRIERS TO THE REFERRAL PROCESS

CLIENT BARRIERS
- Lack of motivation
- Inadequate information about community resources
- Inadequate understanding of the need for referral
- Accessibility needs
- Priorities
- Finances **SDoH**
- Cultural factors **SDoH**

RESOURCE BARRIERS
- Attitudes of health care personnel
- Costs of services **SDoH**
- Physical accessibility of resources
- Time limitations
- Limited expertise working with culturally diverse populations **SDoH**

STEPS IN THE REFERRAL PROCESS

- Engaging in a working relationship with the client
- Establishing criteria for the referral
- Exploring resources
- Accepting the client's decision to use a given resource
- Making the referral
- Facilitating the referral
- Evaluating the outcome

FOLLOW-UP CONSIDERATIONS

- Monitor for completion of the referral.
- Assess whether referral outcomes were met.
- Determine if the client was satisfied with the referral.

DISCHARGE PLANNING

- Discharge planning is an essential component of the continuum of care, and is an ongoing assessment that anticipates the future needs of the client.
- Discharge planning requires ongoing communication between the client, nurse, providers, family, and other members of the interprofessional team. The goal of discharge planning is to enhance the well-being of the client by establishing appropriate options for meeting the health care needs of the client. Qpcc
- Discharge planning begins at admission.

CASE MANAGEMENT

- Case management nursing is indicated for a variety of health care settings and includes the following.
  - Promoting interprofessional services and increased client/family involvement
  - Decreasing cost by improving client outcomes
  - Providing education to optimize health participation
  - Reducing gaps and errors in care
  - Applying evidence-based protocols and pathways
  - Advocating for quality services and client rights
- Collaboration between clients, family members, community resources, payer sources, and health care professionals contributes to successful management of the client's health care needs. Qtc
- Case management nurses must possess excellent communication skills in order to facilitate communication among all parties involved. The case management nurse's ability to articulate the needs of the client to various parties can save time and promote successful outcomes.
- Case management nurses can face ethical dilemmas as they work with consumers and providers to determine the best course of action.

- Case managers are at risk for liability related to five main areas.
  - Care management: Examples of mismanagement include incomplete record keeping, acting in the role of a provider, inappropriate delegation of care, and failing to offer alternative treatments.
  - Referrals: Examples of mismanagement include referring clients to incompetent providers; selecting cheaper, or substandard treatment options and facilities; and failure to communicate with other professionals.
  - Experimental treatments: Examples of mismanagement include failing to notify a client that a treatment is experimental and failing to make recommendations in a timely manner.
  - Confidentiality: Examples of mismanagement include sharing protected information and HIPAA violations.
  - Fraud and abuse: Examples of mismanagement include making false claims or inaccurate information on claims, billing for substandard or unnecessary treatment, and receiving personal compensation for referrals or treatment.
- The nurse uses the nursing process during case management to help the client obtain important services and to treat their condition.
- The nurse provides a link between all facets of the health care experience. This means coordinating care among providers, nursing staff, physical and occupational therapists, rehabilitation facilities, home health care, and community resources.
- The case manager must be proactive for the client, balancing the effect of the illness against the cost of care. Increased knowledge of disease processes promotes early intervention and facilitates transition from acute to community-based care.
- Use of community agencies contains costs, because the monitoring of clients leads to better disease management.

Technology and community nursing

- Technological advances have led to drastic changes in the delivery of health care. The availability of new technologies results in a disruption of old delivery methods, while simultaneously creating new opportunities.
- Some types of technology can assist with cost control. The nurse should compare the expense of new technology to potential cost savings prior to implementation.
- The nurse can use technology as a tool to increase awareness and provide education to clients or to collect data (social media campaigns, electronic surveys, use of health literature databases).
- Technology has had an effect on increasing life expectancy, but also can lead to ethical dilemmas in some situations.
- Nurses must remain informed of new technologies in order to deliver optimal care. The introduction of new technologies can have a significant effect on communities, thus influencing health outcomes.

INFORMATICS AND TELEHEALTH

Informatics

Informatics is the combination of nursing science with information and communication technologies in the delivery of nursing care. Qᵻ

- Electronic health records (EHR), electronic medical records (EMR), databases, and billing are commonly used within the current health care industry. Hand-held computers and smartphones, geographic information systems, and the internet all play a role in the delivery of health care.
- Interprofessional teams and clients can hold meetings electronically. Nurses can use chat rooms and asynchronous discussions as alternative delivery methods for client health education, to facilitate support groups, as a mechanism of peer collaboration, or in staff orientations/training.

Telehealth

Telehealth is the delivery of quality health care through the use of technology.

- Telehealth is particularly useful in rural areas. The ability to deliver specialized, skilled nursing through communication systems that transfer information easily between providers improves access to health care. **SDoH**
- Home care services are increasingly using telehealth technologies in the delivery of client care. Emerging technology allows nurses to provide care to clients at home, while working from a central location, such as an office or health care agency. However, with the use of telehealth, it is important to balance the use of these services with actual hands-on care. A combination of these services is needed for optimal client outcomes.
- Agencies transmitting or storing electronic health data must take measures to ensure confidentiality and security of client information.
- Telecommunication technologies can transmit physical, audio, and visual data.

PHYSICAL DATA
- Blood pressure
- Weight
- Blood oxygenation
- Blood glucose
- Heart rate
- Temperature
- ECG results

AUDIO DATA
- Voice conversation
- Heart sounds
- Lung sounds
- Bowel sounds

VISUAL DATA
- Images of wounds
- Images of surgical incisions

OTHER USES FOR TECHNOLOGY

- Nurses and the interprofessional team can use technology as an outreach tool to educate the public. For example, public service announcements about intimate partner violence have been used to prevent violence and connect community members with appropriate resources.
- Electronic record keeping is widely used in public health to create client clinical records, document services provided, maintain financial records, and for creating and managing organizational plans.

Partnerships with Legislative Bodies

- Decisions and actions made by legislative bodies can have profound effects on health. Health policy specifically addresses health issues within public policy.
- Laws related to health care regulate licensing, define scope of practice and negligent care, and can outline responsibilities in specific settings, such as in schools or correctional facilities.
- Nurses should know about the process required to develop or amend laws that affect the health of the public.
- To facilitate needed change, it is important for nurses to stay informed of current policy and laws that influence both the health of the community and nursing practice. Nurses also should advocate for policies that protect public health or offer solutions to community problems. Qι
- Nurses can influence individuals who develop policies through professional communication and present evidence-based solutions to address significant health problems, decrease health disparities, and ensure equitable distribution of resources. **SDoH**

NURSES' ROLE IN HEALTH POLICY

CHANGE AGENTS: Advocate for needed change at the local, state, or federal level.

LOBBYISTS: Persuade or influence legislators. Individuals or professional nursing associations can participate in the lobbying process.

COALITIONS: Facilitation of goal achievement through the collaboration of two or more groups.

PUBLIC OFFICE: Serve society and advocate for change by influencing policy development through public service.

Application Exercises

1. A nurse is creating partnerships to address health needs within the community. The nurse should be aware that which of the following characteristics must exist for partnerships to be successful? (Select all that apply.)
   A. Being a leading partner with decision-making authority
   B. Flexibility among partners when considering new ideas
   C. Adherence of partners to ethical principles
   D. Varying goals for the different partners
   E. Willingness of partners to negotiate roles

2. A nurse developing a community health program is determining barriers to community resource referrals. Identify the examples of barriers as client barriers or resource barriers.
   A. Costs associated with services
   B. Decreased motivation
   C. Inadequate knowledge about resources
   D. Limited number of service providers
   E. Lack of interpreters

3. A case management nurse is initiating referrals for a client as part of discharge planning. Place in order the actions the nurse should plan to take.
   A. Provide information about the client to the referral agencies.
   B. Monitor client satisfaction with the referral.
   C. Identify referrals the client needs.
   D. Review available resources with the client.

4. A nurse is working with a client who has systemic lupus erythematosus and recently lost their health insurance. Which of the following actions should the nurse take in the implementation phase of the case management process?
   A. Coordinating services to meet the client's needs
   B. Comparing outcomes with original goals
   C. Determining the client's financial constraints
   D. Clarifying roles of interprofessional team members'

5. A nurse is reviewing the various roles of a community health nurse. Match each action to the example of the community health nurse function.

   A. Advocate
   B. Consultant
   C. Coalition builder
   D. Lobbyist
   E. Case manager
   F. Counselor

   1. Updating local officials about the need for activities to prevent youth violence
   2. Contributing to policy development for state funding of prenatal programs
   3. Working with a childcare center on handwashing to reduce the spread of communicable diseases
   4. Collaborating with an interprofessional team to provide continuity of care after hospitalization
   5. Bringing together community agencies to implement a community garden
   6. Establishing an interpersonal relationship with a family to enhance their self-care and coping abilities.

Application Exercises Key

1. A. Being a leading partner with decision-making authority
   B. **CORRECT:** The nurse should recognize that adherence to ethical principles, such as integrity, is essential for a successful partnership, because the nurse and community members are responsible for fulfilling their agreed-upon responsibilities.
   C. **CORRECT:** The nurse should recognize that the willingness to negotiate roles and the distribution of power is essential for a successful partnership, because at every stage of the change process, community members should be active and empowered.
   D. Varying goals for the different partners
   E. **CORRECT:** The nurse should recognize that the willingness to negotiate roles and the distribution of power is essential for a successful partnership, because at every stage of the change process, community members should be active and empowered.

   Ⓝ *NCLEX® Connection: Management of Care, Concepts of Management*

2. **CLIENT BARRIERS:** B, C; **RESOURCE BARRIERS:** A, D, E

   When generating solutions, the nurse should identify decreased motivation and inadequate knowledge as individual characteristics that create barriers to use of resources. The nurse should identify costs, limited number of providers, and lack of interpreters as community characteristics that create barriers to use of resources.

   Ⓝ *NCLEX® Connection: Management of Care, Referrals*

3. C, D, A, B. **CORRECT:** When using the nursing process, first action the nurse should take is to assess the needs of the client to prioritize the types of referrals. After gathering data, the nurse should review available resources with the client to promote self-determination in decision-making. The nurse should next provide information about the client to the referral agencies to facilitate the initiation of services. The last step of the nursing process is evaluating the progress and satisfaction of the client as part of client-centered care.

   Ⓝ *NCLEX® Connection: Management of Care, Referrals*

4. A. **CORRECT:** When taking actions in the case management process, the nurse coordinates services to meet the client through communication and available resources.

   Ⓝ *NCLEX® Connection: Management of Care, Concepts of Management*

5. A, 1; B, 3; C, 5; D, 2; E, 4; F, 6

   When taking actions, the nurse as advocate acts to promote and protect health by actively engaging key decision makers. The nurse as lobbyist uses political strategies to influence policymakers. The nurse as consultant assists others with empowerment to take more responsibility and increase problem-solving skills. The nurse as case manager facilitates communication and resources to implement a plan of care across a continuum. The nurse as coalition builder develops alliances among organizations to solve problems and address health concerns. The nurse as counselor establishes a therapeutic relationship to assist clients in identifying and addressing health concerns.

   Ⓝ *NCLEX® Connection: Management of Care, Concepts of Management*

Active Learning Scenario

A nurse manager of a home health agency is preparing an in-service about informatics for a group of newly licensed nurses. What should the nurse manager include in the presentation? Use the *ATI Active Learning Template: Basic Concept* to complete this item.

RELATED CONTENT
- Define informatics.
- Define telehealth.

UNDERLYING PRINCIPLES
- List two types of transmissible physical data.
- List two types of transmissible audio data.
- List two types of transmissible visual data.

NURSING INTERVENTIONS: Include three methods of incorporating technology into health care delivery.

Active Learning Scenario Key

Using the ATI Active Learning Template: Basic Concept

RELATED CONTENT
- Informatics: The combination of nursing science with information and communication technologies in the delivery of nursing care
- Telehealth: The delivery of quality health care through the use of technology

UNDERLYING PRINCIPLES

Physical data
- Blood pressure
- Weight
- Blood oxygenation
- Blood glucose
- Heart rate
- Temperature
- ECG results

Audio data
- Voice conversation
- Heart sounds
- Lung sounds
- Bowel sounds

Visual data
- Wound images
- Surgical incision images

NURSING INTERVENTIONS
- Electronic records, databases, and billing
- Internet availability of health information and education
- Electronic meetings and chat rooms
- Asynchronous discussions
- Web-based support groups
- Electronic orientation/training
- Health care access in rural areas

Ⓝ *NCLEX® Connection: Management of Care, Information Technology*

References

ATI Nursing. (2022). *Engage community health* (1st ed.).

Berman, A., Snyder, S. & Frandsen, G. (2021). *Kozier & Erb's Fundamentals of nursing: Concepts, process, and practice* (11th ed.) e-book. Pearson.

Burchum, J. R. & Rosenthal, L. D. (2022). *Lehne's pharmacology for nursing care* (11th ed.). Elsevier.

Centers for Disease Control and Prevention. (2018, April 4). *Emergency preparedness and response: Bioterrorism agents/diseases.* https://emergency.cdc.gov/agent/agentlist-category.asp#catdef

Centers for Disease Control and Prevention. (2021, February 26). *Ebola (ebola virus disease): treatment.* https://www.cdc.gov/vhf/ebola/treatment/index.html

Centers for Disease Control and Prevention. (2021, March 10). *About social determinants of health (SDOH).* https://www.cdc.gov/socialdeterminants/about.html

Centers for Disease Control and Prevention. (2021, May 7). *COVID 19 scientific brief: SARS-CoV-2 transmission.* https://www.cdc.gov/coronavirus/2019-ncov/science/science-briefs/sars-cov-2-transmission.html

Centers for Disease Control and Prevention. (2021, September 24). *National Notifiable Diseases Surveillance System (NNDSS): NNDSS supports the COVID-19 response.* https://www.cdc.gov/nndss/action/covid-19-response.html

Centers for Disease Control and Prevention. (2021, October 18). *Smallpox: Prevention and treatment.* https://www.cdc.gov/smallpox/prevention-treatment/index.html

Cherry, B., & Jacob, S.R. (2019). *Contemporary nursing: Issues, trends, & management* (8th ed.). Elsevier.

Coleman-Jensen, A., Rabbitt, M., Gregory, C. A., & Singh, A. (2021, September). Household food security in the United States in 2020. *United States Department of Agriculture: Economic Research Report, 298.* https://www.ers.usda.gov/webdocs/publications/102076/err-298.pdf?v=7386.1

Dudek, S.G. (2022). *Nutrition essentials for nursing practice* (9th ed.). Lippincott, Williams & Wolter.

Ellis, E. (2021, October 11). *Food insecurity and health.* Academy of Nutrition and Dietetics: Eat Right. https://www.eatright.org/health/wellness/your-overall-health/food-insecurity-and-health

Grodner, M., Escott-Stump, S., & Dorner, S. (2020). *Nutritional foundations and clinical applications: A nursing approach* (7th ed.). Elsevier.

Grosenbach, D.W., et al. (2018). Oral tecovirimat for the treatment of smallpox. *The New England Journal of Medicine, 379*(1), 44-53. https://www.nejm.org/doi/pdf/10.1056/NEJMoa1705688?articleTools=true

Halter, M.J. (2022). *Varcarolis' foundations of psychiatric mental health nursing: A clinical approach* (9th ed.). Elsevier.

Hinkle, J.L., Cheever, K.H., & Overbaugh, K.J. (2022). *Brunner & Suddarth's textbook of medical-surgical nursing* (15th ed.). Wolters Kluwer.

Hockenberry, M.J., Wilson, D. & Rodgers, C. (2019). *Wong's nursing care of infants and children* (11th ed.). Elsevier.

Ignatavicius, D.D., Workman, M.L., Rebar, C.R. & Heimgartner, N.M. (2021). *Medical-surgical nursing: Concepts for interprofessional collaborative care* (10th ed.). Elsevier.

MacIntyre, R. (2020). Reevaluating the risk of smallpox reemergence. *Military Medicine, 185*(7/8), e952–e957.

National Center for Health Statistics. (2020, August). *NCHS fact sheet: Healthy people 2030.* https://www.cdc.gov/nchs/data/factsheets/Factsheet-HealthyPeople2030-H.pdf

Office of Disease Prevention and Health Promotion. (2021). *Healthy people 2030.* https://health.gov/healthypeople/objectives-and-data

Office of Disease Prevention and Health Promotion. (n.d.). *Healthy people 2030: Food Insecurity.* https://health.gov/healthypeople/priority-areas/social-determinants-health/literature-summaries/food-insecurity

Potter, P. A., Perry, A. G., Stockert, P. A., & Hall, A. M. (2021). *Fundamentals of nursing* (10th ed.). Elsevier.

Sivanandy, P., et al. (2022). A systematic review of Ebola virus disease outbreaks and an analysis of the efficacy and safety of newer drugs approved for the treatment of Ebola virus disease by the US Food and Drug Administration from 2016 to 2020. *Journal of Infection and Public Health, 15,* 285–292.

Stanhope, M., & Lancaster, J. (2020). *Public health nursing: Population-centered health care in the community* (10th ed.). Elsevier.

Townsend, M. C., & Morgan K. I. (2020). *Essentials of psychiatric mental health nursing: Concept of care in evidence-based practice* (8th ed.) FA Davis

U.S. Department of Health and Human Services. (2018). *National culturally and linguistically appropriate services standards.* https://thinkculturalhealth.hhs.gov/clas/standards

World Health Organization. (2021, December 12). *More than half a billion people pushed or pushed further into extreme poverty due to health care costs.* https://www.who.int/news/item/12-12-2021-more-than-half-a-billion-people-pushed-or-pushed-further-into-extreme-poverty-due-to-health-care-costs

STUDENT NAME _____

CONCEPT_____   REVIEW MODULE CHAPTER_____

Related Content

(E.G., DELEGATION,
LEVELS OF PREVENTION,
ADVANCE DIRECTIVES)

Underlying Principles

Nursing Interventions

WHO? WHEN? WHY? HOW?

STUDENT NAME _____

PROCEDURE NAME _____   REVIEW MODULE CHAPTER_____

Description of Procedure

Indications

Interpretation of Findings

Potential Complications

CONSIDERATIONS

Nursing Interventions (pre, intra, post)

Client Education

Nursing Interventions

STUDENT NAME _____

DEVELOPMENTAL STAGE _____ REVIEW MODULE CHAPTER_____

EXPECTED GROWTH AND DEVELOPMENT

Physical Development	Cognitive Development	Psychosocial Development	Age-Appropriate Activities

Health Promotion

Immunizations	Health Screening	Nutrition	Injury Prevention

ACTIVE LEARNING TEMPLATE: *Medication*

STUDENT NAME _____

MEDICATION _____   REVIEW MODULE CHAPTER_____

CATEGORY CLASS_____

PURPOSE OF MEDICATION

Expected Pharmacological Action

Therapeutic Use

Complications

Medication Administration

Contraindications/Precautions

Nursing Interventions

Interactions

Client Education

Evaluation of Medication Effectiveness

STUDENT NAME _____

SKILL NAME_____   REVIEW MODULE CHAPTER_____

Description of Skill

Indications

CONSIDERATIONS

Nursing Interventions (pre, intra, post)

Outcomes/Evaluation

Client Education

Potential Complications

Nursing Interventions

System Disorder

STUDENT NAME _____

DISORDER/DISEASE PROCESS _____ REVIEW MODULE CHAPTER_____

Alterations in Health (Diagnosis)

Pathophysiology Related to Client Problem

Health Promotion and Disease Prevention

ASSESSMENT

Risk Factors

Expected Findings

Laboratory Tests

Diagnostic Procedures

SAFETY CONSIDERATIONS

PATIENT-CENTERED CARE

Nursing Care

Medications

Client Education

Therapeutic Procedures

Interprofessional Care

Complications

STUDENT NAME _____

PROCEDURE NAME _____ REVIEW MODULE CHAPTER_____

Description of Procedure

Indications

CONSIDERATIONS

Nursing Interventions (pre, intra, post)

Outcomes/Evaluation

Client Education

Potential Complications

Nursing Interventions

STUDENT NAME _____

CONCEPT ANALYSIS_____

Defining Characteristics

Antecedents

(WHAT MUST OCCUR/BE IN PLACE FOR
CONCEPT TO EXIST/FUNCTION PROPERLY)

Negative Consequences

(RESULTS FROM IMPAIRED ANTECEDENT —
COMPLETE WITH FACULTY ASSISTANCE)

Related Concepts

(REVIEW LIST OF CONCEPTS AND IDENTIFY, WHICH
CAN BE AFFECTED BY THE STATUS OF THIS CONCEPT
— COMPLETE WITH FACULTY ASSISTANCE)

Exemplars